Map Projections

Georeferencing spatial data

Contents

Preface

About this handbook

Mapping concepts

Map projection concepts

Contents

Determining a coordinate system

Projection steps

Data management and analysis

Supported map projections

Datums and datum conversion

Glossary

References

Index

Preface

Map projections have fascinated people throughout the ages in many scientific and nonscientific fields. Like mathematics, the subject is self-contained; that is, it is not necessary to conduct physical or chemical tests to determine the validity of a certain approach. Like art, there can be considerable subjective evaluation in choosing one projection over another, especially for world maps. The subject has attracted mathematicians like Gauss, philosophers like Roger Bacon, clergymen like Gall and Braun, physicists like Lambert, astronomers like Cassini, and artists like Dürer, with developments of new projections ranging over the past two thousand years. The fact that the round Earth cannot be flattened onto a plane without distortion means that every flat map must have a projection, however refined or crude.

Until only a couple of decades ago, maps were plotted largely by hand. First a graticule of meridians of longitude and parallels of latitude was laid onto the flat plane using a geometric construction or with the help of a table of coordinates that had been calculated using a table of logarithms or a desktop calculator. Either of these calculating techniques was fairly cumbersome to use. With the advent of high-speed computers, numerous tables of specialized coordinates for graticule intersections could be produced with minimal effort. The geographic information was then manually plotted between the meridians and parallels. When it became possible to enter these computed coordinates for stored points along shorelines and for other geographic features directly into a plotter, mapmaking became highly automated.

It is to serve this modern mapmaking community that ESRI developed the ARC/INFO software system, with map projection computing capability as one of its essential components. The mathematics involved in computing a wide range of projections has been programmed into the software. Much of this projection software originated in the U.S. Geological Survey as the public package *General Cartographic Transformation Package (GCTP)*, but there have been many additions by ESRI.

The programming removes a considerable burden from the user, but this is not enough. The user must also have a sufficient understanding of projections to allow selection not only of an appropriate projection but also of proper related parameters. This understanding should include knowing what to expect when the plot is made, and to be able to recognize a possible error in choice of parameters or in a software program. *Map Projections* is a concise handbook designed to help the user understand the characteristics and purpose of each projection and relevant software feature.

Although some map projections are very complicated, those that are commonly used tend to be conceptually straightforward and can be fun to study by changing the parameters (such as the standard parallels of a conic projection, or the central meridian of a world map projection). Once you understand the principles, plotting can take on some of the satisfactions of traveling in the open country— all sorts of interesting views are possible!

John P. Snyder

Reston, Va.

About this handbook

Map Projections presents the major mapping concepts required to automate and apply spatial data. Early decisions about map coordinate systems and map projections will affect subsequent phases of GIS application, so a thorough grounding in the concepts will enable you to make thoroughly successful applications.

For data automation to be accurate and all subsequent phases of GIS application to be successful, those people who make early decisions about database design must understand map coordinate systems, map projections, datums and their applications. This book supplies a strong conceptual formulation for that understanding.

Overview of *Map Projections*

Mapping Concepts
- Map features
- Map characteristics
  Scale
  Resolution
  Accuracy
- Map extent
- Database extent

Map Projection Concepts
- Shape of the Earth
- Global reference system
  (i.e., latitude, longitude)
- Projection properties
  Conformal
  Equal area
  Equidistant
  True direction

- Planar map surfaces
  - Conic
  - Cylindrical
  - Planar
  - Others
- Other concepts

Procedures and How to's...

- How to use the PROJECT command
- Determining the projection of a base map and other source data
- Defining tic locations
- Establishing a coordinate system for digitizing
- Projecting tic coordinates
- Changing a projection for display or analysis
- Double precision vs. single precision
- Dealing with study areas that cross a 'projection zone'
- Converting a coverage from NAD27 coordinates to NAD83
- Other procedures

This guide presents two primary sets of concepts: fundamental mapping concepts and map projection concepts. A series of procedural discussions in later chapters describe how to apply these concepts to your own geographic database. These 'how to' presentations provide instructions for using ARC/INFO to perform essential data automation and application steps.

Intended audience

The primary audience for this handbook is technical database administrators and project managers. These are the people who will decide which base map to use, how to determine tic locations, what projection to use for data automation, whether coverages should be stored in single or double precision, what projections to use for geographic analysis, reporting, display, and more. At least one person from each site should read and understand this guide.

Chapter 1

Mapping concepts

A map represents geographic features or other spatial phenomena by graphically conveying information about locations and attributes. Locational information describes the position of particular geographic features on the Earth's surface, as well as the spatial relationships between features, such as the shortest path from a fire station to a library, the proximity of competing businesses, and so on. Attribute information describes characteristics of the geographic features represented, such as the feature type, its name or number, and quantitative information such as its area or length.

Map features

Locational information is usually represented by points (for features such as wells and telephone pole locations), lines (for features such as streams, pipelines, and contour lines) and areas (for features such as lakes, counties, and census tracts).

Point feature

A point feature represents a single location. It defines a map object too small to show as a line or area feature. A special symbol or label usually depicts a point location.

Line feature

A line feature is a set of connected, ordered coordinates representing the linear shape of a map object that may be too narrow to display as an area, such as a road, or a feature with no width, such as a contour line.

Area feature

An area feature is a closed figure whose boundary encloses a homogeneous area, such as a state, county, soil type or lake.

Map characteristics

In addition to feature locations and their attributes, the other technical characteristics that define maps and their use include scale, resolution, accuracy, and projection.

Map scale

To show a portion of the Earth's surface on a map, the area must be reduced. Map scale, or the extent of reduction, is expressed as a ratio. The number on the left indicates distance on the map; the number on the right indicates distance on the ground. The following three statements show the same scale:

1 inch = 2,000 feet
1 inch = 24,000 inches
1:24,000

The latter is known as a representative fraction (RF) because the amounts on either side of the colon are equivalent; that is, '1:24,000' means '1 inch equals 24,000 inches' or '1 foot equals 24,000 feet' or '1 meter equals 24,000 meters', and so on.

Map scale indicates how much the given area was reduced. For the same size map, features on a small-scale map (1:1,000,000) will be smaller than those on a large-scale map (1:1,200).

So each scale represents a different trade-off. With a small-scale map, you'll be able to show a large area without much detail. With a large-scale map, you'll be able to show a lot of detail but not as much area. The three maps shown below illustrate the trade-off. The small-scale map can show a large area because it reduces the area so much; the large-scale map can only show a portion of one street, but in such detail that you can see the shapes of the houses.

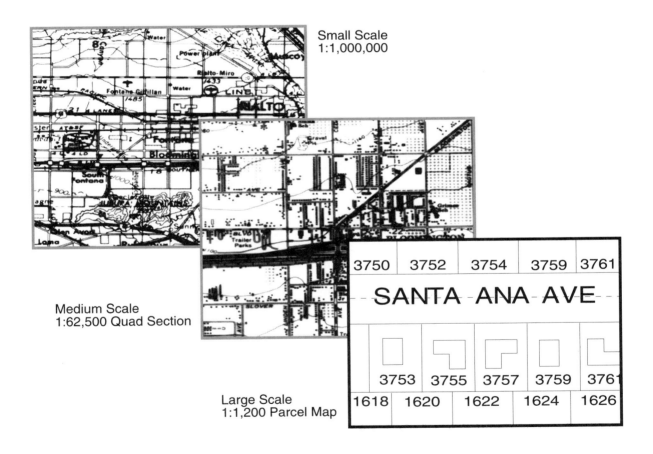

Small Scale
1:1,000,000

Medium Scale
1:62,500 Quad Section

Large Scale
1:1,200 Parcel Map

3750	3752	3754	3759	3761

SANTA ANA AVE

3753	3755	3757	3759	3761
1618	1620	1622	1624	1626

On certain United States Geological Survey topographic maps, the Universal Transverse Mercator (UTM) grid tics are 10,000 meters apart and are shown in blue along the edge of the map. You can use these grid tics to verify the scale of the map by measuring the distance between the tics with a ruler. The distance on the map in relation to the ground distance (10,000 meters) gives you a statement of scale. For example, the distance between the UTM tics on the map is 1.6 inches, and the distance between the UTM tics on the ground is 10,000 meters. The verbal statement of scale is 'one point six inches on the map equals ten thousand meters on the ground', or 1.6 inches equals 10,000 meters.

To convert this statement to a representative fraction, the units of measure being compared must be the same. For this example, both measurements will be in meters.

To do this, convert 1.6 inches into meters:

1.6 inches x .0254 meters/inch = 0.04 meters

Now you know that

0.04 units on the map = 10,000 units on the ground

You can now state the scale as a representative fraction (RF):

0.04:10,000

Though a valid statement of scale, most cartographers would find it clumsy. Traditionally, the first number in the representative fraction is made equal to 1:

$$\frac{0.04}{0.04} = 1 \text{ unit on the map} = \frac{10{,}000}{0.04} \text{ units on the ground}$$

1 unit on the map = 250,000 units on the ground

After this calculation, you can see that 1 unit on the map equals 250,000 units on the ground, or 1:250,000.

The equation for calculating map scale is:

$$\frac{1}{RFD} = \frac{MD * CON}{GD}$$

RFD = Representative Fraction Denominator (i.e., in a 1:24,000 topographic map the RFD = 24,000)

MD = Map Distance

GD = Ground Distance

CON = Conversion Factor to relate MD and GD; thus, if MD is measured in inches and GD is measured in miles, CON = 63,360 (the number of inches in 1 mile)

The following diagram compares lengths of lines representing one kilometer at different map scales. The greater the scale, the longer the line.

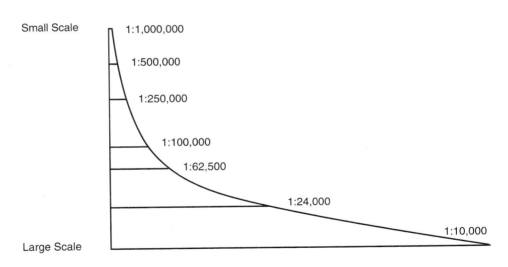

Each line represents one kilometer at its respective scale.

Map resolution

Map resolution refers to how accurately the location and shape of map features can be depicted for a given map scale. Scale affects resolution. In a larger-scale map, the resolution of features more closely matches real-world features because the extent of reduction from ground to map is less. As map scale decreases, the map resolution diminishes because features must be smoothed and simplified, or not shown at all. For example, at a scale of 1:63,360 (in which 1 inch = one mile), it is difficult to represent area features smaller than 1/8 of a mile wide or 1/8 of a mile long, because they will be 1/8 of an inch wide or long on the map.

As scale decreases, long narrow features such as streams and roads must be represented as lines and smaller area features as points. The minimum sizes and dimensions are sometimes called *minimum mapping units*. When maps are being compiled, the minimum mapping units might be stated as a series of rules to follow. For example, 'long narrow features such as streams and rivers will be represented as lines if their width is less than 1/8 inch. If a polygon is smaller than 1/8 inch on a side, it will be represented as a point', and so on.

Scale	2 cm	4 cm^2		1 in	1 in^2
1:24,000	0.48 km	23.04 ha		0.38 mi	91.80 ac
1:62,500	1.25 km	156 ha		0.99 mi	623.00 ac
1:100,000	2.00 km	400 ha		1.58 mi	1594.00 ac
1:250,000	5.00 km	2,500 ha		3.95 mi	9964.00 ac
1:500,000	10.00 km	10,000 ha		7.89 mi	39856.00 ac

	0.2 cm	0.04 cm^2		1/8 in	1/16 in^2
1:24,000	0.05 km	0.23 ha		0.38 mi	1.44 ac
1:62,500	0.13 km	1.56 ha		0.99 mi	9.73 ac
1:100,000	0.20 km	4.00 ha		1.58 mi	24.90 ac
1:250,000	0.50 km	25.00 ha		3.95 mi	156.00 ac
1:500,000	1.00 km	100.00 ha		7.89 mi	623.00 ac

Comparison of mapping units at five scales.

Map accuracy

Many factors besides resolution influence how accurately features can be depicted, including the quality of source data, the map scale, your drafting skills, and the width of lines used to represent features. Suppose you were drafting map features at a scale of 1:63,360. (Remember that one inch on such a map represents one mile on the ground.) A fine drafting pen will draw lines 1/100 of an inch wide. Such a line represents a corridor on the ground which is almost 53 feet wide.

width is 53 feet

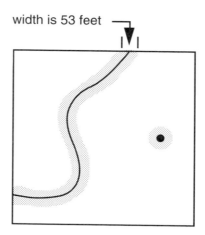

In addition, human drafting errors will occur and can be compounded by the quality of your source maps and materials.

Even though no maps are entirely accurate, they are still useful for decision-making and analysis. However, it is important to consider map accuracy to ensure that your data is not used inappropriately.

Any number of factors can cause error. Note that these sources can have a cumulative effect.

$$E = f(f) + f(l) + f(c) + f(d) + f(a) + f(m) + f(p) + f(rms) + f(mp) + u$$

where,

f = flattening the round Earth onto a two-dimensional surface (transformation from spherical to planar geometry)

l = accurately measuring location on Earth (correct projection and datum information)

c = cartographic interpretation (correct interpretation of features) d = drafting error (accuracy in tracing of features and width of drafting pen)

a = analog to digital conversion (digitizing board calibration)

m = media stability (warping and stretching, folding, wrinkling of map)

p = digitizing processor error (accuracy of cursor placement)

rms = Root Mean Square (registration accuracy of tics)

mp = machine precision (coordinate rounding by computer in storing and transforming)

u = additional unexplained sources error

To minimize error, consider the causes of each error factor presented above. To choose the pen size appropriate to your map's scale, for instance, use the following table:

Scales						
Pen Size		4,800	24,000	62,500	100,000	2,000,000
000	.0099 in	3.9	19.7	51.2	82	1640
	(.25 mm)	(1.2)	(6.0)	(15.6)	(25.0)	(500.0)
00	.0118 in	4.6	23.6	61.7	98.4	1968
	(.30 mm)	(1.4)	(7.2)	(18.8)	(30.0)	(600.0)
0	.0138 in	5.5	27.6	71.8	114.8	2296
	(.35 mm)	(1.7)	(8.4)	(21.9)	(35.0)	(700.0)
1	.0197 in	7.9	39.4	102.7	164.0	3281.0
	(.50 mm)	(2.4)	(12.0)	(31.3)	(50.0)	(1,000.0)

Pen width on the ground is displayed in feet (and meters).

The National Map Accuracy Standards were established for the U.S. in 1941 by what is now the Office of Management and Budget (OMB). These standards state that

■ No more than 10 percent of features shall be more than 1/30th of an inch from their intended location on maps of scale larger than 1:20,000.

■ No more than 10 percent of features shall be more than 1/50th of an inch from their intended location on maps of scale smaller than 1:20,000.

One way to ensure an acceptable level of accuracy is to overlay the map manuscript with a check plot of the newly digitized coverage. All features should be represented at a level of accuracy wherein no visible gap may be seen between lines on the two map sheets when overlaid. Any space between the manuscript line and the digitized line is considered unacceptable error. Use a 000 (.25 mm) pen or smaller for drafting manuscripts and plotting check plots with this technique.

Map extent

The areal extent of a map is the area on the Earth's surface represented on the map. It is the limit of the area covered, usually defined by a rectangle just large enough to include all mapped features. The size of the study area depends on the map scale. The smaller the scale the larger the area. The maps in the scale comparison example earlier in this chapter show the effect of scale on map extent. The smaller-scale map on the left covers a greater area than the more detailed larger-scale map on the right.

Database extent

A critical first step in building a geographic database is defining its extent. The areal extent of a database is the limit of the area of interest for your GIS project. This usually includes the areas directly affected by your organization's responsibility (such as assigned administrative units) as well as surrounding areas that either influence or are influenced by relevant activities in the administrative area.

Once you have defined the extent of your database, decide on a base map series to which each coverage layer of your database will be referenced. Such layers often register to a single map series, such as the USGS 7.5-minute quadrangle map sheets. But sometimes layers are derived from maps at a variety of scales and resolutions, so they need to be registered to a common base. The map projection of these base maps will determine which coordinate system your coverages will initially be stored in. Each map series provides the projection definition used to produce each map sheet.

Data automation

Map features are logically organized into sets of layers or themes of information. A base map can be organized into layers such as streams, soils, wells, or boundaries. Map data, regardless of how a spatial database will be applied, is collected, automated, and updated as a series of adjacent map sheets (or aerial photographs)— each sheet mounted on the digitizer and digitized, one sheet at a time. In order to be able to combine these smaller sheets into larger units or *study areas,* the coordinates of each coverage must be transformed into a single common coordinate system. Once in a common coordinate system, attributes are associated with features. Then, as needed, map sheets for a layer are edgematched and joined into a single coverage for your study area.

Mapping concepts

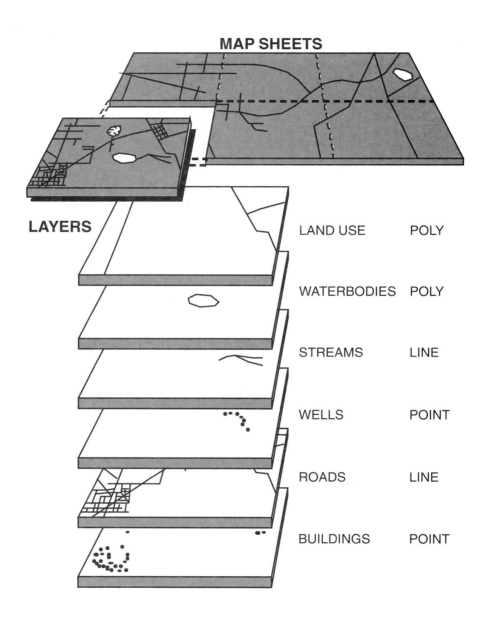

MAP SHEETS

LAYERS

LAND USE   POLY

WATERBODIES   POLY

STREAMS   LINE

WELLS   POINT

ROADS   LINE

BUILDINGS   POINT

Sometimes adjacent map sheets in the same study area do not conform to the same map projection definition. For example, UTM or STATE PLANE zones may change between two adjacent map sheets. (For further discussion, see 'Crossing zonal boundaries' in Chapter 5, 'Data management and analysis'.)

Summary

■ Large scale equals large detail.

■ Scale, resolution, accuracy and content of a map are all related.

■ Map data are grouped spatially (by map sheet or photo) and thematically (by layers).

■ Each layer of a database is referenced to a particular base map.

■ The map projection and coordinate properties of a base map define the original coordinate system of each map sheet layer to be automated.

■ All layers of a spatial database should be stored in a common coordinate system.

■ All sources of spatial data are referenced by some map projection.

■ Data automation is most often done on a layer-by-layer and map sheet-by-map sheet basis.

■ When combining data at a variety of scales, resolutions, and accuracies, the combined data sources should be considered to be only as good as the worst input.

Chapter 2

Map projection concepts

Maps are flat, but the surfaces they represent are curved. Transforming three-dimensional space onto a two-dimensional map is called 'projection'. Projection formulas are mathematical expressions which convert data from a geographical location (latitude and longitude) on a sphere or spheroid to a representative location on a flat surface. This process inevitably (unavoidably) distorts at least one of these properties—shape, area, distance, direction—and often more. Since measurements of one or more of these (distorted) properties are often used to make decisions, anyone who uses maps as analytical tools should know which projections distort which properties, and to what extent. Briefly, *conformal* maps preserve local shape, *equal-area* or equivalent maps retain all areas at the same scale, *equidistant* maps maintain certain distances, and *true-direction* maps express certain accurate directions.

The shape of the Earth

Although it is actually a spheroid, the Earth is sometimes treated as a sphere to make mathematical calculations easier. Its radius is valued, in ARC/INFO, at 6,370,997 meters. This assumption that the Earth is a sphere can be used for small-scale maps, those less than 1:5,000,000. At this scale, the difference between a sphere and a spheroid cannot be detected on a map. However, to maintain accuracy for larger-scale maps (scales of 1:1,000,000 or larger), the Earth must be treated as a spheroid.

As a sphere is based on a circle, so a spheroid (or ellipsoid) is based on an ellipse. The shape of an ellipse is defined by two different radii. The longer axis is called the major axis and the shorter axis is known as the minor axis. The respective radius of each axis is termed the semi-major and the semi-minor axis.

The difference in magnitude between the two axes of an ellipse can be expressed as a fraction or a decimal. This value is used to define its degree of ellipticity or flattening.

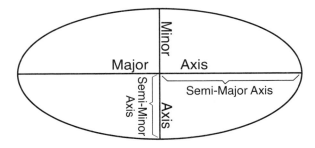

Values of ellipticity range between 0 and 1. An ellipticity of 0 means the two axes are equal, resulting in a circle. An ellipticity of 1 means the figure would have only one axis, appearing as a straight line, whose length would equal the length of the major axis. In general, large elliptical values describe narrow ellipses, and small elliptical values represent almost circular ellipses.

Just as rotating a circle about an axis defined by its diameter will create a sphere, rotating an ellipse about either its major or minor axis will produce an ellipsoid. An *ellipsoid* which approximates a sphere is called a *spheroid*. An ellipsoid which approximates the shape of the Earth is formed by rotation around the minor axis.

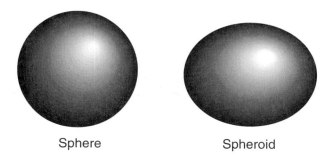

Sphere   Spheroid

The ellipticity of a sphere is 0.0, whereas the ellipticity of the Earth is approximately 0.003353. The flattening phenomenon is observed at the poles, and the bulging occurs at the Equator. Therefore, the semi-major axis describes the equatorial radius, and the semi-minor axis represents the polar radius.

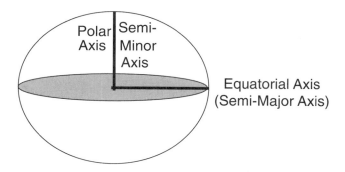

Polar Axis | Semi-Minor Axis

Equatorial Axis (Semi-Major Axis)

Defining different spheroids for accurate mapping

The Earth has been surveyed many times to better understand its surface features and their peculiar irregularities. From these surveys, many spheroids for the Earth have been defined. The semi-major and semi-minor axes that best fit one geographical region are not necessarily the same ones that fit another region. Until recently, values determined by Clarke in 1866 have been used to describe the spheroid commonly used with the reference datum for North America; this is often referred to as the *North American Datum 1927* (NAD27). The semi-major axis of this spheroid is 6,378,206.4 meters, and the semi-minor axis has been calculated as 6,356,583.8 meters.

Because of gravitational variations and variations in surface features, the Earth is neither a perfect sphere nor a perfect spheroid. Satellite technology has revealed several elliptical deviations; for example, the South Pole is closer to the Equator than the North Pole. It should be noted that satellite-determined spheroids are starting to replace the ground-measured spheroids for reference calculations. A factor that must be taken into account before changing spheroids of reference is the effect that such a change will have on all previously measured values. Because of the complexity of changing spheroids, ground-measured spheroids are currently still in use and are still valid points of reference. For additional discussion of spheroids and datums, refer to Appendix B.

ARC/INFO supports twenty-six spheroids. Their names, axis values and the geographical locations to which they apply (where available) are listed in the table 'Semi-major and Semi-minor Axes of Spheroids'. You will notice that the measurements do vary, but only by a small quantity relative to the magnitude of the Earth.

Semi-major and Semi-minor Axes of Spheroids
(Axes values in meters. These are the values used by the PROJECT command.)

Name	Date	Semi-major Axis (a)	Semi-minor Axis (b)	Use
Airy	1830	6377563.396	6356256.91	Great Britain
Australian National		6378160	6356774.719	
Bessel	1841	6377397.155	6356078.96284	Most parts of Central Europe, Chile and Indonesia
Clarke	1866	6378206.4	6356583.8	North American Continent and Philippines
Clarke	1880	6378249.145	6356514.86955	France, and most of Africa
Everest	1830	6377276.3452	6356075.4133	India, Burma, Ceylon, Malaysia (part)
Fischer	1960	6378166	6356784.28	
Fischer	1968	6378150	6356768.33	
GRS80	1980	6378137	6356752.31414	North America
Helmert	1907	6378200	6356818.17	Egypt
Hough		6378270	6356794.343479	
International	1909	6378388	6356911.94613	
Krasovsky	1940	6378245	6356863.0188	USSR and some East European countries
Modified Airy		6377341.89	6356036.143	

Name	Date	Semi-major Axis (a)	Semi-minor Axis (b)	Use
Modified Everest		6377304.063	6356103.039	
Modified Fischer	1960	6378155	6356773.32	
Modified Mercury	1968	6378150	6356768.337303	
Mercury	1960	6378166	6356784.283666	
New International	1967	6378157.5	6356772.2	
South American	1969	6378160	6356774.72	
Southeast Asia		6378155	6356773.3205	
Sphere		6370997	6370997	
Walbeck		6376896	6355834.8467	
WGS66		6378145	6356759.769356	
WGS72		6378135	6356750.519915	World wide
WGS84	1984	6378137	6356752.31	World wide

Measurements on the globe

Although degrees of latitude and longitude can be used to locate exact positions on the surface of the globe, they are not uniform units of measure on the Earth's surface. Only along the Equator does the distance represented by one degree of longitude approximate the distance represented by one degree of latitude. This is because the Equator is the only parallel as large as a meridian. (Circles with the same radius as the spherical Earth are called *great circles*. Within the graticular network, all meridians and the Equator are *great circles*.)

The degrees of latitude and longitude aren't associated with a standard length, and so can't be used as an accurate measure of distance. And because this reference system measures angles from the center of the Earth, rather than distances on the Earth's surface, it's not a planar coordinate system. Similarly, because the global coordinate system is used for the curved surface of the Earth, this system cannot be called a map projection. It would be more accurate to say that values of latitude and longitude serve as reference positions on the surface of the Earth for all available map projections. Because of this ability to reference locations, the spherical coordinate system is also known as the Global Reference System. The units of degrees, minutes, and seconds are often useful for referencing points on base maps.

Spherical measurements

Even though a flat surface, or planar geometry is easier to conceptualize, understanding map projections begins with understanding spherical geometry. In the spherical system, all horizontal lines are called lines of latitude or *parallels*. The vertical lines are called lines of longitude or *meridians*. These lines encompassing the globe form a gridded network called a *graticule*.

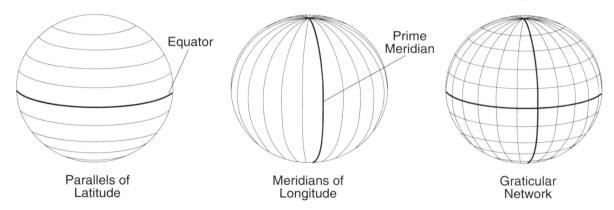

Parallels of
Latitude

Meridians of
Longitude

Graticular
Network

Above and below the Equator, the circles defining the parallels of latitude get gradually smaller until they become a single point, the North Pole or the South Pole. The poles are also where meridians converge. As the meridians converge toward the poles, the distance represented by one degree of longitude decreases until it equals zero. On the Clarke 1866 spheroid, one degree of longitude at the Equator equals 111.321 km, while at 60° latitude it is only 55.802 km.

Viewing the North Pole as 'up', the horizontal 'axis' is called the Equator and the vertical 'axis' is called the Greenwich Prime Meridian. The origin is defined by the intersection of the Greenwich Prime Meridian and the Equator. Like the Cartesian origin, its coordinates are (0,0). The sphere is then divided into four geographical quadrants based on compass bearings from the origin. Above and below the Equator are north and south, and to the right and left of the Greenwich Prime Meridian are east and west.

Latitude and longitude are angles measured from the Earth's center to a point on the Earth's surface. Latitude and longitude define the location of points on the globe. They reference the angles of a line extending from the center of the Earth to the Earth's surface to a spherical coordinate system.

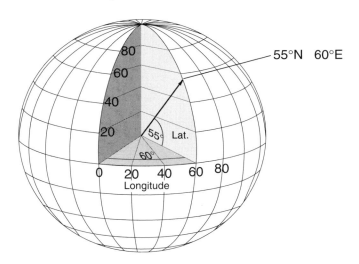

A circle can be divided into 360 units called degrees. Each degree can be further subdivided into sixty minutes, and each minute into sixty seconds.

Latitude and longitude are traditionally measured in degrees, minutes, and seconds (DMS). For latitude, 0° is at the Equator, 90° is at the North Pole, and -90° is at the South Pole. For longitude, 0°, the Prime Meridian, starts at the North Pole, passes through Greenwich, England, and ends at the South Pole. Longitude is measured positively, up to 180°, when traveling east from Greenwich and measured negatively, to -180°, traveling west from Greenwich. For example, Australia, which is south of the Equator and east of Greenwich, has positive longitudes and negative latitudes.

Latitudes on a spheroid are measured perpendicular to the surface, not from the center of the spheroid as on a sphere, but the difference is small.

Planar measurements

Because it is difficult to make measurements in spherical coordinates, geographic data is projected into a planar coordinate system. Once the sphere, or portion, is projected onto a flat surface, the spherical values change. On a flat surface, locations are identified by x,y coordinates on a grid, with the origin at the center of the grid. Each position has two values which reference it to that central location, one specifying its horizontal position and the other its vertical position. These two values are called the x-coordinate and y-coordinate. Using this notation, the coordinates at the origin are x = 0 and y = 0.

On a gridded network, constructed of equally spaced horizontal and vertical lines, the horizontal line in the center is called the x-axis and the central vertical line is called the y-axis. Equal spacing represents units consistent across the full range of x and y. Horizontal lines above the origin and vertical lines to the right of the origin are assigned positive values; those below or to the left are negative. The four quadrants represent the four possible combinations of positive and negative x and y coordinates.

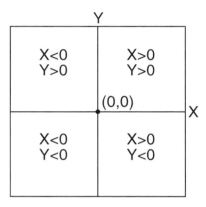

The advantage of a planar system is that measures of length, angle, and area are constant across the two dimensions.

Properties of map projections

Whether you treat the Earth as a sphere or as a spheroid, you must transform its three-dimensional surface to create a flat map sheet. This transformation, usually using a mathematical conversion, is commonly referred to as *map projection*. One easy way to understand how map projections alter spatial properties is to visualize projecting a light through the Earth onto a surface, called the projection surface.

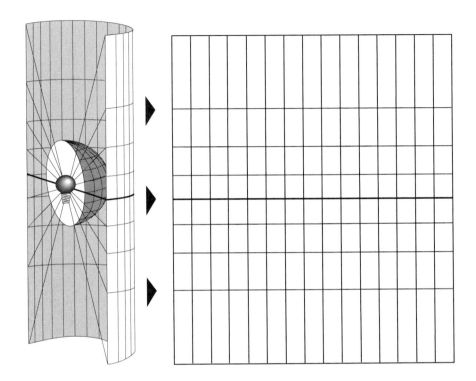

The projection of a map involves the use of coordinates as defined by projection formulas. The formulas can transform an input coverage into an output coverage that is similar, but on a completely different projection. The result is that intersections are maintained, but the angles at which they intersect may be altered. The following diagram shows how three-dimensional features are compressed to fit onto a flat surface. Stretching can also result.

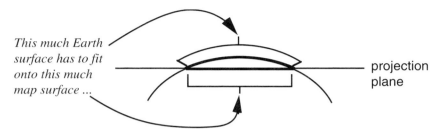

This much Earth surface has to fit onto this much map surface ...

projection plane

therefore, much of the Earth surface has to be represented smaller than nominal scale.

Conformal projections

Conformal projections preserve local shape. Graticule lines on the globe are perpendicular. To preserve individual angles describing spatial relationships, a conformal projection must also present graticule lines intersecting at 90-degree angles on the map. This is accomplished by maintaining all angles, including those between intersections of arcs. The drawback is that the area enclosed by a series of arcs may be greatly distorted in the process. No map projection can preserve shapes of larger regions.

Equal-area projections

Equal-area projections preserve the area of displayed features. To do this, the properties of shape, angle, scale, or any combination of these may be distorted. Thus, in such projections, the meridians and parallels may not intersect at right angles. In some instances, especially maps of smaller regions, it will not be obvious that shape has been distorted, and distinguishing an equal-area projection from a conformal projection may prove difficult unless documented or measured.

Equidistant projections

Equidistant maps preserve the distances between certain points. Scale is not maintained correctly by any projection throughout an entire map; however, there are, in most cases, one or more lines on a map along which scale is maintained correctly. Most projections have one or more lines for which the length of the line on a map is the same length (at map scale) as the line it references on the globe, regardless of whether it is a great or a small circle, straight or curved. Such distances are said to be *true*. For example, in the SINUSOIDAL projection, the Equator and all parallels are their true lengths. In other equidistant projections, the Equator and all meridians may be true. Still others (e.g., TWO_POINT_EQUIDISTANT) show true scale between one or two points and every other point on the map. Keep in mind that no projection is equidistant to and from all points on a map.

True-direction projections

The shortest route between two points on a curved surface such as the Earth is along the spherical equivalent of a straight line on a flat surface; that is, the great circle on which the two points lie. True-direction or *azimuthal* projections are used to rectify some of the great-circle arcs, giving the directions or azimuths of all points on the map correctly with respect to the center. There are projections of this type that are also conformal, or equal-area, or equidistant.

Projection types

Because maps are flat, some of the simplest projections are made onto geometric shapes that can be flattened without stretching their surfaces. Common examples of shapes that meet this criterion are cones, cylinders, and planes. Actually, cylinders and planes are limiting forms of a cone. A mathematical expression that systematically projects locations from the surface of a sphere to representative positions on a planar surface is called a *map projection*.

The first step in projecting from one surface to another is to create one or more points of contact. Each point is called a *point of tangency*. As illustrated below, a planar projection is tangential to the globe at one point only. Tangential cones and cylinders contact the globe along a line. If the surface of projection intersects the globe instead of merely touching its surface, the resultant projection conceptually involves a secant calculation rather than a tangential calculation. Whether the contact is tangent or secant, the location is significant because it defines the point or lines of zero distortion. This line of true scale is often referred to as a *standard line*. In general, projection distortion increases with distance from the point of contact.

Many common map projections can be classified according to the projection surface used for each: conic, cylindrical and planar. ARC/INFO supports forty-six projections. The names of these and their classifications are listed in the table at the end of this chapter.

Conic projections

The most simple conic projection is tangent to the globe along a line of latitude. This line is called the *standard parallel* for a given projection. The meridians are then projected onto the conical surface, meeting at the apex. Parallel lines of latitude are projected onto the cone as rings. The cone is then 'cut' along any meridian to produce the final conic projection, which has straight converging meridians and concentric circular arcs for parallels. The meridian opposite the cut line becomes the *central meridian*.

Tangent conic projections convert coordinates on the Earth to a cone. The line along which the cone touches the surface of the Earth is called the standard parallel.

In general, distortion increases north and south of the parallel of tangency. Thus, cutting off the top of the cone produces a more accurate projection. This can be accomplished by not using the polar region of the projected data, a technique used for mid-latitude zones that have an east-to-west orientation.

Somewhat more complex conic projections can be thought of as contacting the global surface at two locations. These projections are called *secant* conic projections and are defined by two standard parallels. The distortion for secant projections is not the same for those regions between the standard parallels as it is for the regions beyond the standards. This explains why the resultant conic projection from a secant cone is different from one produced by a tangent cone. On still more complex conic projections, the axis of the cone does not line up with the polar axis of the globe. These are called *oblique*.

Secant conic projections also convert coordinates on the Earth to a cone. But unlike tangent conic projections, secant conic projections conceptually contact the surface of the Earth along two lines. Consequently, there are two standard parallels.

The representation of geographic parameters depends on the spacing between the parallel lines. When equally spaced, the projection is equidistant in the north-south direction but not conformal and not equal-area, such as the Equidistant Conic projection (EQUIDISTANT). For small areas, the overall distortion is minimal. On the Lambert Conic Conformal projection (LAMBERT) the central parallels are spaced more closely than the parallels near the border, and small geographic shapes are maintained for both small-scale and large-scale maps. Finally, on the Albers Equal-Area Conic projection (ALBERS), the parallels near the northern and southern edges are closer together than the central parallels, and the projection will display equivalent areas.

Cylindrical projections

Cylindrical projections may also have one line of tangency or two lines of secancy around the globe. The Mercator projection is one of the most common cylindrical projections, and the Equator is usually its line of tangency. Meridians are geometrically projected onto the cylindrical surface, and latitude parallels are mathematically projected, producing graticular angles of 90 degrees. The cylinder can be 'cut' along any meridian to produce the final cylindrical projection. The meridians are equally spaced, while the spacing between parallel lines of latitude increases toward the poles. This projection is conformal and displays true direction along straight lines. *Rhumb lines*, lines of constant bearing, but not most great circles, are straight lines.

For more complex cylindrical projections the cylinder is rotated, thus changing the lines used for tangency or secancy. Transverse cylindrical projections such as the Transverse Mercator use meridians as their tangential contact, or lines parallel to meridians as lines of secancy. Their lines of tangency then run north and south, along which the scale is true. Oblique cylinders are rotated around a great-circle line located anywhere between the Equator and the meridians. In these more complex projections, most meridians and the lines of latitude are no longer straight.

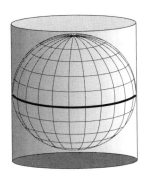

Normal

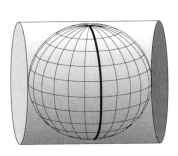

Transverse

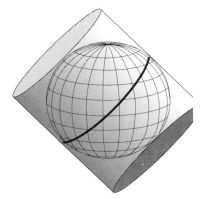

Oblique

In all cylindrical projections, the line of tangency or lines of secancy have no distortion and thus are lines of equidistance. Other geographical properties vary depending on the specific projection.

Planar projections

Planar projections project map data onto a flat surface touching the globe. A planar projection is the same kind of projection as an azimuthal projection or a zenithal projection. This kind of projection is usually tangent to the globe at one point, but may be secant. The point of contact may be the North Pole, the South Pole, a point along the Equator, or any point in between. This point specifies the *aspect* used and functions as the focus of the projection. The focus is identified by a central longitude and a central latitude; and possible aspects are *polar*, *equatorial*, and *oblique*.

Polar

Equatorial

Oblique

Polar aspects are the simplest form of this kind of projection. Latitude parallels radiate from the pole as concentric circles, and meridians are represented by straight lines which intersect at the pole with their true angles of orientation. In all other aspects, planar projections will have graticular angles of 90 degrees at their central focus. Directions from the focus are accurate. Great circles passing through the focus are represented by straight lines, thus the shortest distance from this point to any other point on the map is a straight line. Patterns of areal and conformal distortion are circular about the focus. For this reason, azimuthal projections accommodate circular regions better than rectangular regions. Planar projections are used most often to map polar regions.

Some planar projections view surface data from a specific point in space. This point of view determines where the spherical data will be projected onto a flat surface. The perspective from which all locations are viewed varies between the different azimuthal projections. Perspective points may be the center of the Earth, a surface point directly opposite from the tangential point, or a point external to the globe, as if seen from a satellite or another planet.

Azimuthal projections are differentiated in part by their focus and, if applicable, by the perspective point. The following diagram compares three perspective projections with polar aspects but different perspective positions. The GNOMONIC projection views the surface data from the center of the Earth, whereas the STEREOGRAPHIC projection views it from one pole to the opposite pole. The ORTHOGRAPHIC projection views the Earth from an infinite point, as if viewed from deep space. Note how the differences in perspective determine the amount of distortion towards the Equator.

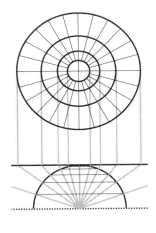

Gnomonic

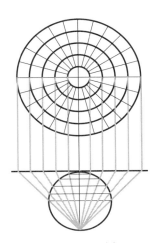

Stereographic

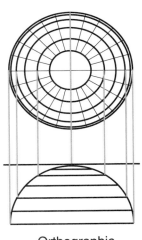

Orthographic

Other projections

The projections discussed thus far are projections that can be conceptually created by projecting from one geometric shape (a sphere) onto another (a cone, cylinder, or plane). Many other projections cannot be related as easily to one of these three surfaces.

Modified projections are modified versions of another projection (e.g., the Space Oblique Mercator is a modification of the Mercator projection). These modifications are made to reduce distortion, often by including additional standard lines or a different pattern of distortion.

Pseudo projections have only some of the characteristics of another class of projection. For example the Sinusoidal is called a pseudocylindrical projection because all lines of latitude are straight and parallel, and all meridians are equally spaced. However, it cannot truly be a cylindrical projection because all meridians except the central meridian are curved. This results in the Earth appearing oval instead of rectangular.

Other categories may be assigned to special groups, such as circular, star, and so on.

Chapter 3

Determining a coordinate system

For any database to be useful for spatial analysis, all its parts must be registered to a common coordinate system. Before automating any data, you must determine an appropriate coordinate system in which to store the database. You must determine how the data will be referenced, and you must establish a set of control points in a common coordinate system.

Determine projection characteristics of input

To find information about the projection used to create a map, look at its legend. The legend of a map may list a projection by name and give its parameters, such as Lambert Conformal Conic with standard parallels at 34°02' and 35°28', and origin at 118° W, 33°30' N. Or it may list a coordinate system and zone number, such as California Coordinate System zone 5, or State Plane Coordinate System zone 3376, all of which, in this case, define the same projection and parameters. If the legend doesn't contain information about projections refer to the section 'Maps without coordinate information' in Chapter 5.

It is also important, especially for large-scale maps, to know the spheroid used. The U.S. standard was Clarke 1866 (for NAD27), but the standard is being converted to GRS80 (for NAD83), which is discussed in greater detail in Appendix B. The spheroid is sometimes inherent to a coordinate system, such as Clarke 1866 for older State Plane maps, or GRS80 for newer ones.

Mapped, edited and published by the Geological Survey

Control by USGS, NOS/NOAA, and USCE

Topography by photogrammetric methods from aerial photographs taken 1975. Field checked 1976. Map edited 1981.

Projection and 10,000-foot grid ticks: California coordinate system, zone 5 (Lambert conformal conic)

1000-meter Universal Transverse Mercator grid, zone 11
1927 North American Datum

Example of coordinate and projection information in the legend of a USGS 7.5' quadrangle.

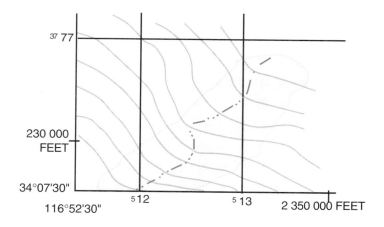

Example of coordinates from three different systems on a USGS 7.5' quadrangle.

Along the margins of most maps, you will find one or more sets of coordinates that reference locations on the Earth's surface. On a USGS 7.5' series map, three types of coordinates are provided: the projection of the map, along with Universal Transverse Mercator meters and latitude-longitude degrees.

For small-scale maps containing multiple coordinate systems, there is an additional consideration. All map projections distort the Earth in different ways, therefore, lines of equal coordinate value may have different curvatures.

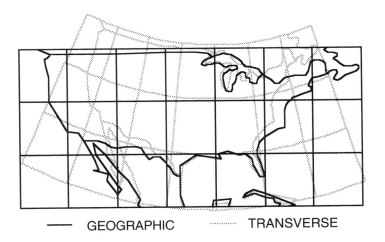

—— GEOGRAPHIC   ········· TRANSVERSE

For this reason, it is best to use graticular intersections on the map. In contrast to drawing straight lines across a map to connect coordinates on either side, graticule lines may be represented by curved lines. This is less of a concern for large-scale maps. It is not a problem for equatorial aspects of cylindrical projections, such as MERCATOR.

Choosing a map projection

When deciding upon the projection in which to store your database, consider the database's primary use.

■ Databases created under contract or to be used by a governmental organization are often in a projection determined by the governing body, such as State Plane in the United States or Great Britain National Grid in Great Britain.

■ Use equal-area projections for thematic or distribution maps.

■ Presentation maps are usually conformal projections, although compromise and equal-area projections can also be used.

■ Navigational maps are usually Mercator, true direction and/or equidistant.

Other considerations:

■ The extent of the area to be mapped. Is it a database of the world, a continent, a state?

■ Location of the area to be mapped. Is it a polar, mid-latitude, or equatorial region?

■ Predominant extent of the area to be mapped. Is the area roughly circular, or longer in the east-west, north-south, or some oblique direction?

The list below shows a range of choices for common map types.

World

Conformal
    MERCATOR, TRANSVERSE, OBLIQUE_MERCATOR
Equal-Area
    CYLINRICAL, ECKERTIV, ECKERTVI,
    FLAT_POLAR_QUARTIC, MOLLWEIDE, SINUSOIDAL

Equidistant
 AZIMUTHAL
Straight rhumb lines
 MERCATOR
Compromise
 MILLER, ROBINSON

Hemisphere

Conformal
 STEREOGRAPHIC, POLAR
Equal-Area
 LAMBERT_AZIMUTH
Equidistant
 AZIMUTHAL
Global look
 ORTHOGRAPHIC

Continent or smaller region

Predominantly east-west along Equator
 Conformal
  MERCATOR
 Equal-Area
  CYLINDRICAL
Predominantly east-west away from Equator
 Conformal
  LAMBERT
 Equal-Area
  ALBERS
Predominantly north-south
 Conformal
  TRANSVERSE, UTM
Predominantly oblique
 Conformal
  OBLIQUE_MERCATOR

Equal extent in all directions
    Conformal
        POLAR, STEREOGRAPHIC, UPS

    Equal-Area
        LAMBERT_AZIMUTH
Straight great-circle routes
        GNOMONIC
Correct scale
    Between points
        TWO_POINT_EQUIDISTANT
    Along meridians
        AZIMUTHAL (polar aspect), EQUIDISTANT,
        EQUIRECTANGULAR, SIMPLE_CONIC
    Along parallels
        POLYCONIC, SINUSOIDAL, BONNE

Based upon Snyder 1987, Map Projections—A Working Manual

Chapter 4

Projection steps

After determining the projection of the data sources and deciding upon a projection in which to store the database, it is time to use this information. It is time to project your data into a real-world coordinate system. Registering all layers to a common coordinate system ensures data integrity during spatial joins.

Digitizer units vs. real-world coordinates

Coverages may be digitized in digitizer units or real-world units. The digitizer is based on a type of rectangular coordinate system with its origin in the lower-left corner. On the digitizer surface, moving one inch up or down covers the same distance as moving one inch left or right. Anywhere on the table's surface, an inch is an inch. Whether the unit of measure be inches or centimeters, when associated with digitizing it is called a *digitizer unit*.

Location and distance are key when mapping geographic features. The real world has a curved surface and is often measured in feet or meters. Both feet and meters are standard units of measure, but they do not have an obvious global origin. Therefore, the system of spherical coordinates (Global Reference System) is used to reference specific locations on the surface of the globe with points on a map. The units of this reference system are degrees of latitude and longitude. But the distance represented by a degree depends upon its location on the globe; that is, the Global Reference System is not a rectangular coordinate system. Thus, a coverage can be digitized in meters, but not in degrees.

The advantages and disadvantages of digitizing a coverage in either digitizer units or in real-world units are outlined in the following table and explained in the paragraphs that follow.

Digitizer Units	vs.	Real-World Units
Easy to create edit plots at scale of source map		Maps need to be plotted at a precise scale to overlay edit plots
Digitizing staff has less to learn and understand		Digitizing staff should understand transformation and projection concepts
Coverages are not spatially referenced and can't be displayed simultaneously		Allows multiple coverages to be shown, such as background or adjacent coverages
Inconvenient for update		Usually used for update
Less concern over bad projection information		Must have correct projection parameters
Don't know whether initial digitizing of tics was accurate		RMS error indicates actual tic accuracy in real-world units

A common step in quality assurance when initially developing a database is to compare a digitized file to its source map. This is most commonly done by creating an edit plot and overlaying it on a light table. If a map is digitized in real-world units, it may have been stretched and scaled so that it will no longer register accurately with the source map, even if the file was digitized accurately.

If coverages are to be digitized in real-world units, the digitizing staff should understand how to project and transform coverages. This requires some knowledge of projection concepts, as discussed in Chapter 2.

The ability to display adjacent and background coverages can be quite helpful, particularly when updating maps. This is not possible when maps are digitized in digitizer units.

Coverages should not be edited, cleaned, built, or buffered, nor should any spatial analysis be performed when they are stored in reference units (latitude-longitude). The algorithms that perform snapping functions or maintain topology that use a measurement of length or area are based upon Cartesian coordinates. The length of a line of latitude between two meridians varies with latitude, and area is confusing when measured in square degrees.

Steps for Digitizing in Digitizer units	Steps for Digitizing in Real-world units
Register map	Digitize or CREATE tics
Digitize tics and features	Project tics
Create tics	Register map
Project tics	Digitize features
Transform coverage into real-world coordinates using projected tics	

Step 1: Establish tics

A tic is a registration or geographic control point for a coverage. Tics register coverage coordinates to a common coordinate system (e.g., UTM meters, State Plane feet, etc.) and, therefore, relate locations of features in a coverage to locations on the Earth's surface.

Points representing tics can be located on maps by identifying the x- and y-coordinates from a known real-world coordinate system. These are usually stated in both map projection units (usually meters or feet) and degrees of latitude and longitude. Often real-world coordinates for these tics are taken straight from an original map. It is also possible to use latitude and longitude values to identify geographic registration points that will then be projected to coordinates of the desired projection.

Find at least four points common to each map sheet whose location on the map as control points and coordinate values can be easily determined for each layer of the database. It is recommended to establish a *master tic file*—a file to which all layers are referenced.

There is no standard way to number tics, simply establish a consistent procedure. One common guideline is to use a regular numbering system, always increasing in the same direction, and not back and forth across the maps. If you are using map sheet corners as the tic locations, the coincident location on adjacent maps are commonly given the same Tic-ID.

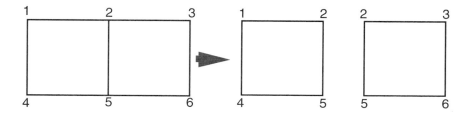

Tic table

Once you have numbered the tics, and determined the coordinate location for each, arrange them in a table. Keep this table in a notebook with other important database information. You will need it for future reference when transforming the maps to real-world coordinates.

Tic-ID	Latitude	Longitude
1	41 03 45	-74 00 00
2	41 03 45	-73 59 15
3	41 03 45	-73 58 30
4	41 03 00	-74 00 00
5	41 03 00	-73 59 15
6	41 03 00	-73 58 30

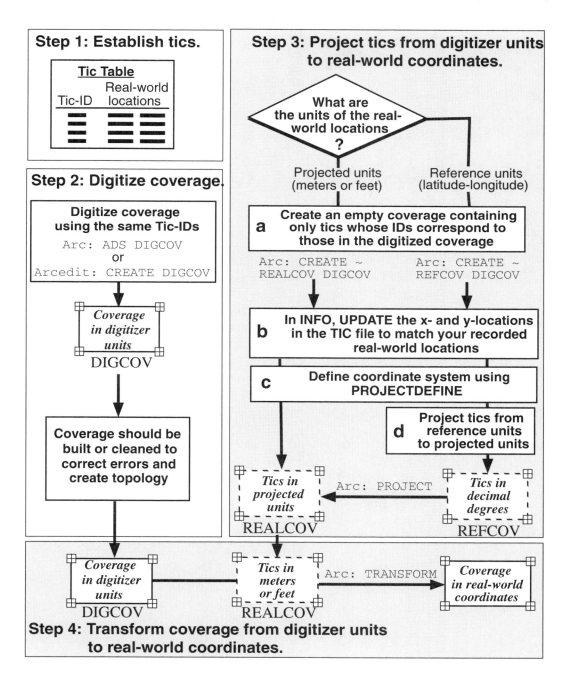

The flowchart on the preceding page outlines the process used to create a coverage in digitizer units and then convert it to real-world coordinates.

Step 2: Digitize coverage

For a discussion on how to digitize a coverage refer to 'Editing coverages and tables with ARCEDIT'.

Step 3: Project tics from digitizer units to real-world coordinates

This step will convert the tics of your digitized coverage (DIGCOV) from digitizer units to spherical coordinates (REFCOV) and then to projection coordinates (REALCOV). Assume that the digitized map contains six tic locations and that locational references for each tic were marked on the original map manuscript using a latitude-longitude graticule. The following table was developed using the TIC table created in Step 1. It establishes both updated Tic-IDs and their real-world locations. Note that the real-world locations are referenced in degrees, minutes, and seconds.

Real-world locations

Tic-ID	X (longitude)	Y (latitude)
22	-74° 00 minutes 00 seconds	41° 03 minutes 45 seconds
23	-73 59 15	41 03 45
24	-73 58 30	41 03 45
32	-74 00 00	41 03 00
33	-73 59 15	41 03 00
34	-73 58 30	41 03 00

Before proceeding, convert these real-world locations from degrees, minutes and seconds (DMS) into decimal degrees (DD). Given that there are 60 seconds in a minute, and 60 minutes in a degree, decimal degrees can be computed using the following equation:

Decimal Degrees = Degrees + Minutes/60 + Seconds/3600

Here is a table showing both DMS and decimal degrees.

Real-world locations

Tic-ID	X (in DMS)	X (in DD)	Y (in DMS)	Y (in DD)
22	-74 00 00	-74.0000	41 03 45	41.0625
23	-73 59 15	-73.9875	41 03 45	41.0625
24	-73 58 30	-73.9750	41 03 45	41.0625
32	-74 00 00	-74.0000	41 03 00	41.0500
33	-73 59 15	-73.9875	41 03 00	41.0500
34	-73 58 30	-73.9750	41 03 00	41.0500

Step 3a: Creating an empty coverage containing only tics

The tic and boundary files for a new coverage can be created by using the ARC command CREATE to copy the TIC and BND files from an existing coverage. You want to use the same Tic-IDs, so use the TIC and BND files from your clean, digitized coverage (DIGCOV) to create an empty coverage (REFCOV). The tics' coordinates are in digitizer units.

Step 3b: Updating tic coordinates to latitude-longitude locations

Once generated, the TIC file (REFCOV) can be updated in INFO with the real-world coordinates recorded from the original map. This lets you convert digitizer values into their corresponding latitude and longitude locations. When tic locations are measured in meters or feet, they represent the projected coordinate system of the base map. If these locations are from a graticule measuring degrees of latitude and longitude, they are reference locations only, and haven't yet been projected.

The easiest way to edit coordinate values is in INFO using UPDATE. Refer to the TIC table you developed previously for the new tic values. Be sure to

■ Match the Tic-IDs correctly

■ Enter the coordinates in decimal degree values

■ Record each XTIC value (i.e., longitude) as a negative number, if you are in the western hemisphere

The display of XTIC and YTIC values only includes three significant digits (the XTIC and YTIC items are always defined as floating point binary with three decimal places used for display). The stored tic values retain their full precision with which they were entered. The values have been rounded off for display only.

```
ENTER COMMAND> LIST
$RECNO    IDTIC        XTIC         YTIC
    1        22      -74.000      41.063
    2        23      -73.988      41.063
    3        24      -73.975      41.063
    4        32      -74.000      41.050
    5        33      -73.988      41.050
    6        34      -73.975      41.050
```

Step 3c: Defining the coordinate system using PROJECTDEFINE

The ARC command PROJECTDEFINE records the coordinate system of the data. This information then is forever carried with the data and can be used for future transformations.

```
Arc: PROJECTDEFINE
Usage: PROJECTDEFINE<COVER | GRID | FILE | TIN> <target>
```

```
Arc: PROJECTDEFINE COVER REFCOV
Define Projection
Project: PROJECTION GEOGRAPHIC
Project: UNITS DD
Project: PARAMETERS
Arc:
```

Step 3d: Projecting the tics from reference units to projected units

If the current real-world tic locations are referenced by latitude and longitude, then they are said to be in reference units (degrees), rather than projected units (meters or feet). Before you can perform the transformation, these locations must be projected into the base map projection. If the tic locations were recorded in Step 3b in projected map coordinates (i.e., meters or feet), then this step is not necessary and the transformation process would directly convert the existing digitizer measurements to real-world coordinates.

The original base map from which DIGCOV was generated used the Universal Transverse Mercator (UTM) projection. Therefore, we'll project the tic coordinates recorded in decimal degrees of latitude-longitude into UTM meters. These will form the basis for the real-world coordinates into which the new coverage will ultimately be transformed.

Projections can be performed either automatically with a text file of parameters or by interactively entering the projection definition. The output projection definition corresponds to the projection of the base map as well as to the other coverages in the study area database.

A text file used to input the projection definition must follow the format outlined on the following page. When the projection definition is entered interactively, the INPUT projection is read from the PRJ file of the source data, and only the OUTPUT projection definition can be entered.

INPUT	Table 1: PROJECTION Options	
PROJECTION < 1 >	ALASKA_E	LOCAL
	ALASKA_GRID	MERCATOR
UNITS < 2 >	ALBERS	MILLER
	AZIMUTHAL	MOLLWEIDE
< 3 >	BIPOLAR_OBLIQUE	NEWZEALAND_GRID
	BONNE	OBLIQUE_MERCATOR
	CASSINI	ORTHOGRAPHIC
PARAMETERS	CHAMBERLIN	PERSPECTIVE
Projection-specific parameter	CRASTER_PARABOLIC	POLAR
definition for output coverage	CYLINDRICAL	POLYCONIC
	ECKERTIV	ROBINSON
OUTPUT	ECKERTVI	RSO
	EQUIDISTANT	SIMPLE_CONIC
PROJECTION < 1 >	EQUIRECTANGULAR	SINUSOIDAL
	FLAT_POLAR_QUARTIC	SPACE_OBLIQUE_MERCATOR
UNITS < 2 >	GALL_STEREOGRAPHIC	STATEPLANE
	GEOCENTRIC	STEREOGRAPHIC
< 3 >	GEOGRAPHIC	TIMES
	GREATBRITAIN_GRID	TRANSVERSE
PARAMETERS	GRINTEN	TWO_POINT_EQUIDISTANT
Projection-specific parameter	HAMMER_AITOFF	UPS
definition for output coverage	LAMBERT	UTM
	LAMBERT_AZIMUTH	

Table 2: UNITS Options	Table 3: Optional Subcommands	
DD (decimal degrees)	DATUM	SPHEROID
DM (decimal minutes)	DENSIFY	XSHIFT
DMS (degrees minutes seconds)	FIPSZONE	YSHIFT
DS (decimal seconds)	FLIP	ZONE
FEET	FORMAT	ZUNITS
METERS	GENERALIZE	QUIT
RADIANS	QUADRANT	
Real Number (units/meter)		

This figure illustrates the structure of the PROJECT subcommand usage.

```
Arc: PROJECT
Usage: PROJECT <COVER | GRID | FILE> <input> <output>
       {projection_file} {NEAREST | BILINEAR | CUBIC}
       {out_cellsize}
GEO_UTM.PRJ
INPUT
PROJECTION GEOGRAPHIC
UNITS DD
PARAMETERS
OUTPUT
PROJECTION UTM
UNITS METERS
ZONE 18
XSHIFT -580000
YSHIFT -4540000
PARAMETERS
END

Arc: PROJECT COVER REFCOV REALCOV GEO_UTM.PRJ
Arc:
```

The optional subcommands are described in the PROJECT
command reference, and projection options are described in detail
in Appendix A.

Step 4: Transform the coverage from digitizer units to real-world coordinates

The ARC command TRANSFORM changes coverage coordinates
using either an *affine* or a *projective* transformation function. The
affine transformation function—which is based on three or more
control points (tics)—calculates change in scale, shift in the
x-direction, shift in the y-direction and any rotation for the output
coverage. The projective transformation compensates for a linear
tilt in the z dimension. It should be used when transforming oblique
aerial photos, but not with maps. The transformation scale
describes the difference in the scale from the input coverage to
output coverage coordinates. This scale factor is shown in the

report generated as part of the TRANSFORM command processing.

The transformation function is applied uniformly to all coordinates, scaling, rotating, and shifting all features in the output coverage. Straight lines remain straight after transform (i.e., transform will not add additional vertices to two-point arcs). Consider densifying the data before using TRANSFORM. This also holds true when projecting a coverage containing two-point arcs, where you can use the DENSIFY option in PROJECT.

Before using TRANSFORM, you should have an output coverage containing only the projected tics, REALCOV. TRANSFORM uses corresponding Tic-IDs to compare the input coverage tics to those of the output coverage. The calculated transformation is applied to all feature coordinates in the input coverage as they are copied to the output coverage. Thus all feature coordinates are transformed into UTM meters for the output coverage. The original coverage, DIGCOV, is not altered in any way by TRANSFORM.

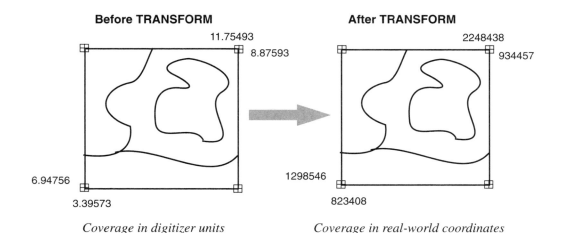

Coverage in digitizer units   *Coverage in real-world coordinates*

```
Arc: TRANSFORM
Usage: TRANSFORM <in_cover> <out_cover>
                {AFFINE | PROJECTIVE}

Arc: TRANSFORM DIGCOV REALCOV AFFINE
Transforming coordinates for coverage DIGCOV
```

TRANSFORM generates and displays a report on the screen showing comparisons between input and output coverage tics, the parameters used for the transformation, and measures of how accurately the two coverages fit together.

```
Scale (X,Y) = (1452.240,1508.545)
Translation = (2124994.654,317664.386)
Rotation (degrees) = (0.218)
RMS Error (input,output) = (0.048,71.627)
```

tic id	input x output x	input y output y	x error	y error
1	2.000	16.946		
	2127791.000	343183.000	14.463	75.500
2	12.764	16.821		
	2143469.000	343326.000	-31.043	-85.362
3	2.052	1.976		
	2128000.000	320680.000	-36.290	-2.352
4	12.922	2.013		
	2143729.000	320912.000	20.245	-6.162
5	2.082	9.442		
	2127944.000	332015.000	22.016	-74.700
6	12.662	9.442		
	2143320.000	332015.000	10.609	93.077

The RMS error describes the deviation between the tic locations in the input coverage and those in the output coverage. Although it never occurs with real-world data, a perfect transformation would produce an RMS error of 0.000. The RMS error for each transformation is reported in both input coverage units (0.048 inches) and output coverage units (71.627 meters).

The affine transformation is derived using least squares.

$$\text{RMS error} = \sqrt{\frac{e_1^2 + e_2^2 + e_3^2 + \bullet \bullet \bullet + e_n^2}{n}}$$

⊞   Input coverage tics

⊞   Transformed location
     of input coverage tics

↺   Errors

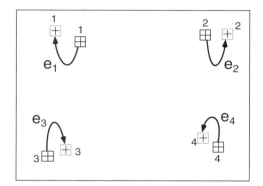

■   Acceptable values will vary depending on the accuracy of the original data and the scale of the source map.

■   A perfect transformation produces an RMS error of 0.000.

■   High RMS errors indicate that the old tics and the new tics do not correspond to the same relative locations.

■   Establish and maintain a maximum acceptable error. Keep your RMS error as low as possible. (If your digitizer units are inches, your RMS should usually be less than 0.005.)

■   If your RMS error is higher than the established acceptable value, it can indicate conversion problems that may incorrectly distort your output coverage.

Determine an acceptable RMS value by examining your data and the scale it represents. For real geographic databases, keep your RMS error as low as possible.

High RMS errors indicate that the input and output coverage tics do not match well, and that the output coverage features will not register well with the original source map. This can happen for a number of reasons, including original coverage tics were not digitized accurately.

■ There is map sheet distortion such as stretching or shrinking.

■ The real-world coordinate values for tics were not recorded correctly; for example, an x- and y-coordinate value might be flipped for one of your tics.

Registering maps without coordinate information

Occasionally, you will need to use a map that contains little or no coordinate information. This is a problem if you intend to register this map with another. Although the following method doesn't register the maps perfectly, it does provide a reasonable option.

Assume that you need to register map A with no coordinate information to map B whose coordinates are known. Both are already coverages. (Read the command references for steps with which you are unfamiliar.)

1) Select 4 widely spaced points, common to maps A and B, to be used as tics for A.

2) In ARCEDIT, using EDITFEATURE TIC, ADD the locations of these new tics to A.

3) CREATE a new coverage, A2, using A as the {tic_bnd_cover}.

4) In INFO, UPDATE the tic coordinates of A2 using the coordinate information taken from B in Step 1.

5) TRANSFORM A using coordinates in A2. This will perform a linear coordinate shift of all values. Only the tics with Tic-IDs in both coverages will be used for the transformation.

6) In ARCEDIT, with EDIT A2, EDITFEATURE LINK, DRAWENVIRONMENT ARC LINK, BACKENVIRONMENT ARC, and BACKCOVERAGE B, select easily identifiable

common points and use ADD to add links. You need at least four links; using more should improve your results. Some of these points should be near the extreme edge of the coverages to ensure that the entire coverage is adjusted.

7) Use ADJUST to rubber sheet the features of A2 nearer to their correct locations in B. ADJUST creates a TIN to perform the rubber sheeting, so any features outside the links will not be adjusted.

When using data registered in this manner, consider the sources of error. The result will be no more accurate than the least accurate input. The smaller the scale of the maps the higher the degree of error. Do not use this procedure to build a database from poorly documented maps, particularly if measurements or decisions are to be based upon the results.

Chapter 5

Data management and analysis

The database is complete, and all parts are stored in a common coordinate system. Now it's time to think about how to analyze and manage your data: what secondary projections and transformations to use to register new data or output graphics, how to handle study areas that cross projection zones, and how single and double precision affect your final data.

Secondary projections

Sometimes you will need to change the projection of a data set, either to change the properties of a map or to combine two maps with different projection characteristics. Changing the projection of a map that is already stored in a real-world coordinate system is referred to as a *secondary projection*.

When the projection in which the database is stored does not produce the desired properties of a map, the projection can be changed. For example, if your database is stored in a conformal projection, and you want to use an equal-area projection for distribution mapping, you might change from a Mercator to a Mollweide. Or if your database is a Sinusoidal and you want to emphasize a polar region, you might use the Polar Stereographic. Another common reason to change the projection of a data set is to combine data from more than one zone of a projection, such as UTM or State Plane. (Refer to the section 'Crossing zonal boundaries' later in this chapter.)

Although changing from one projection to another is accomplished with a single command, it is actually a two-step process. The first step changes the projection of the data from what it was stored in to geographic coordinates on a sphere or spheroid. This is referred to as *inverting* the projection. The next step changes it to the desired output projection. This is referred to as the *forward* transformation of the projection.

You can perform a secondary projection in one of two ways: at the ARC level with PROJECT, or in ARCPLOT using MAPPROJECTION. If you may need the newly projected coverage in the future, use PROJECT, because it will create a new coverage. If you only need the projected coverage for a one-shot graphic, or just to see how it would look, use MAPPROJECTION, which only creates a display.

The MAPPROJECTION command is also useful for simultaneously displaying multiple data sets from many projections in a common projection. This can be done by setting the input projection to AUTO and the output projection to the desired projection.

Secondary Projections

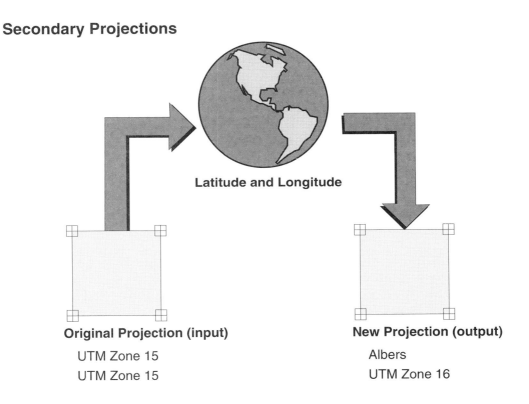

Latitude and Longitude

Original Projection (input)

UTM Zone 15
UTM Zone 15

New Projection (output)

Albers
UTM Zone 16

Summary of points for secondary projections:

- Data has already been automated
- Used to match existing data in another coordinate system
- Used to highlight different properties of the data (area vs. shape)
- Coordinates retain a real-world meaning

Secondary transformations

To create special graphic effects of layered or perspective tiles of a database, apply a secondary transformation. This technique is commonly used to show how the layers of a database coregister to the same geographic location, exhibiting different characteristics or themes with each layer. Note, however, that secondary transformations leave the coordinates of the coverages without real-world meaning.

To perform a secondary transformation, first determine how the data should be layered. Will it be vertical, skewed, or arranged otherwise? What direction and magnitude of shift is needed to achieve the desired effect?

The key to this process, as shown in the following diagram, lies in changing the top (ymax) of the map. It is normally either reduced in length symmetrically, or shifted to the right or left. It is also necessary to reduce the range of y.

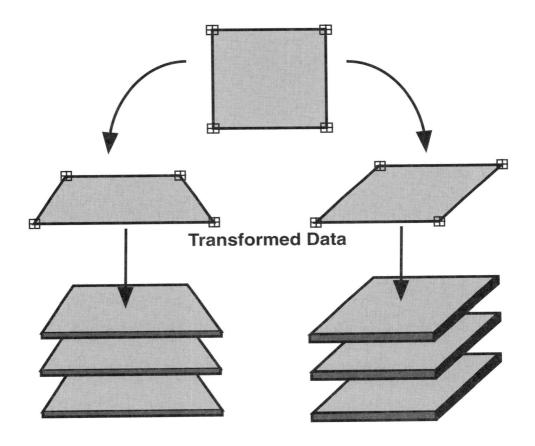

Transformed Data

Crossing zonal boundaries

Coordinate systems such as State Plane and UTM use zones to minimize distortion. Often a study area crosses two zones, and features at the edge of these zones do not match. There are two ways to perform analysis on an area falling in two zones. The first and easiest way is to project one of the coverages into the zone of the adjoining coverage. In the example below, zone 10 was projected to zone 11 because the majority of the study area falls in zone 11.

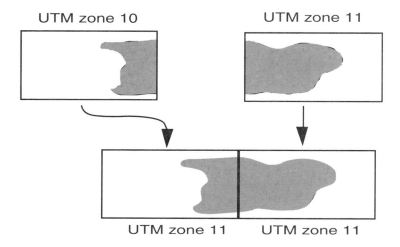

The other method for joining zones is to project both coverages into a different projection that has no zones. That different projection is usually the base projection of the original zone, such as Lambert Conic Conformal (LAMBERT) or Transverse Mercator (TRANSVERSE). (For additional guidelines on selecting a projection, refer to 'Choosing a map projection' in Chapter 3, 'Determining a coordinate system'.)

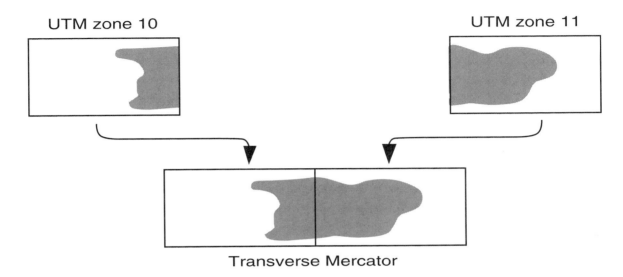

UTM zone 10

UTM zone 11

Transverse Mercator

Be aware that both methods will increase the amount of error caused by projection distortion. Error will increase with distance from the standard lines of the projection. To determine the severity of this error, plot the original zone and the extended zone together and note their differences.

Coverage precision

ARC/INFO coverages can be stored in either single- or double-coordinate precision and used interchangeably; for example, you can display single- and double-precision coverages over each other, overlay them, merge them, and so on. This capability, however, does not negate the need to be clear and deliberate about how you encode, store and manage each coverage. Base your decision of which precision to use upon the desired level of coordinate accuracy to be maintained for each coverage.

Single-precision coverages can store up to seven significant digits for each coordinate. This means that a precision of one meter can be maintained for a coverage whose extent is 1,111,111 units across. (This is somewhat system dependent.) Still, users often require higher levels of precision. Further, the coordinate systems for many map projections use much larger coordinate values (e.g., State Plane and UTM coordinates contain values in the 2,000,000 to 6,000,000 range). In these cases, you can use double-precision coordinates to maintain accuracy of less than one unit (i.e., beyond the decimal point).

Double-precision coverages can store up to fifteen significant digits. This is sufficient to map any point on the Earth to better than a millimeter of accuracy. However, double-precision coverages require additional storage space. Thus, it may be worthwhile to store coverages that require high levels of accuracy (such as parcels) in double precision and less accurate coverages (such as soils) in single precision.

Changing the precision of a coverage is simple provided that you know the coordinate system you plan to use. Before converting between single- and double-precision coordinates, establish whether all layers in your database are referenced to the same origin. If not, then use the TRANSFORM command to perform the conversion between single and double precision. If all layers are already in the same coordinate system, then use the COPY command to convert the precision of a coverage.

Estimating the costs of double-precision coordinate

Double-precision coverages are not twice as large as single-precision coverages. All coverages are composed of a set of x,y coordinates which represent feature locations, along with topological and attribute information. Only the coordinates are stored in double precision. Coverages with many curvilinear arcs (such as soils) require more coordinate storage than do coverages with many two-point arcs (such as streets and parcels coverages).

Additionally, coverages with many attributes, such as parcels, will use less total disk space for storing coordinates.

As a general rule, coverages with more coordinates require a larger proportion of storage for coordinates; therefore, their size will increase more dramatically for double-precision storage. For example, we have found that double-precision parcel coverages require up to ten percent more storage, while soils coverages may require up to twenty percent more. Similarly, as the file increases in size, the I/O processes of the computer (e.g., during copying and editing) also increase. (ARC/INFO has used double precision for internal computations for many years; therefore, the actual processing speed of internal computations is unchanged.)

When to use double precision

It is probably best to use double precision if the coordinate resolution of a coverage must be maintained past six significant digits. Here are some of the conditions that meet this requirement:

■ Your coverage requires a high level of accuracy, such as a parcels layer.

■ Your study area is quite large and cannot be represented with the desired coordinate precision because of the differences in coordinate extremes (e.g., your study area is 2,000,000 feet wide and you require 5-foot accuracy).

■ You need to use a map projection whose coordinate values exceed the available coordinate precision. Alternatively, apply coordinate offsets and still use single-precision coordinates. (See 'Maintaining accuracy in single precision' below.)

■ You are changing datums, such as NAD27 to NAD83.

Setting PRECISION coordinates

The PRECISION command defines the coordinate precision of new and derived coverages created during an ARC/INFO session. PRECISION establishes two rules: creation and processing.

Creation rule

Specifies the precision with which to create all new coverages. This can be set to SINGLE or DOUBLE. Anytime a new coverage is created (such as with the CREATE command in ARCEDIT), the coordinate precision of the new coverage will be defined by the current creation rule. SINGLE is the default. Thus, if you want to create double-precision coverages, you must set the creation rule to DOUBLE with the PRECISION command at the Arc: prompt before running CREATE in ARCEDIT.

Processing rule

Specifies the precision with which to create all derived coverages. This can be set to LOWEST, HIGHEST, SINGLE or DOUBLE. Anytime a new coverage is derived from one or more existing coverages (such as the result of BUFFER, UPDATE or APPEND), the coordinate precision of the new coverage will reflect the current processing rule. For example, the output coverage precision can be the HIGHEST of a set of input coverages. Thus, if all input coverages are in single precision, the output coverage will be single precision; if at least one of the coverages is double precision, then the output coverage will be double precision; and so on. To create double-precision coverages regardless of the precision of the input coverages, set the processing rule to DOUBLE with the PRECISION command before you begin.

Maintaining accuracy in single precision

Coordinate offsets can often be used to maintain coordinate accuracy in single-precision coverages. Coordinate offsets are created by subtracting a constant value from the x-coordinate, y-coordinate or both. This operation, known as translation, can be performed with the TRANSFORM command or by using the XSHIFT and YSHIFT options of the PROJECT command. To maintain coordinate accuracy, the coverage must be created using tics to which the coordinate offset has already been applied. Alternatively, the coverage can be created in double precision and transformed into a single-precision coverage using coordinate offsets.

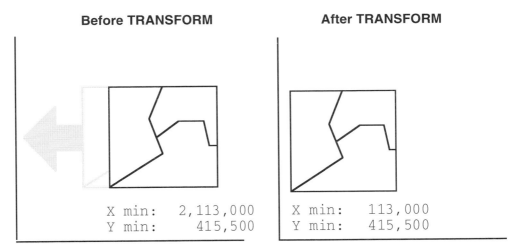

| **Before TRANSFORM** | **After TRANSFORM** |

| X min: 2,113,000 | X min: 113,000 |
| Y min: 415,500 | Y min: 415,500 |

Perform coordinate translation with the TRANSFORM command.

Converting between single and double precision

There are two alternative approaches to changing coordinate precision in a coverage: one is to translate (shift) coordinates; the other is to copy the coverage. Translation, as discussed above, can be used to maintain accuracy. However, all layers in your database must also be translated. The table below identifies the command sequences to use in each case for converting the precision of a coverage. Following the table is a more complete example of converting a double-precision coverage to single precision.

Operation		Command sequence
Copy from single to double precision	Converting without regard to coordinate accuracy	`Arc: COPY <sgl_cov> <dbl_cov> DOUBLE`

	Converting single-precision coverages by translation to maintain accuracy	`Arc: PRECISION SINGLE DOUBLE`
		`Arc: CREATE <dbl_cov> <sgl_cov>`
		
		`Info: SELECT <dbl_cov>.TIC`
		`Info: CALC XTIC = XTIC + <x_offset>`
		`Info: CALC YTIC = YTIC + <y_offset>`
		
		`Arc: TRANSFORM <sgl_cov> <dbl_cov>`

Copy from double to single precision	Converting without regard to coordinate accuracy	`Arc: COPY <dbl_cov> <sgl_cov> SINGLE`

	Converting double-precision coverages by translation to maintain accuracy	`Arc: PRECISION SINGLE HIGHEST`
		`Arc: CREATE <new_cov> <dbl_cov>`
		Note: <new_cov> is created and transformed in double precision, and copied as a single-precision coverage.
		
		`Info: SELECT <new_cov>.TIC`
		`Info: CALC XTIC = XTIC - <x_offset>`
		`Info: CALC YTIC = YTIC - <y_offset>`
		
		`Arc: COPY <new_cov> <sgl_cov> SINGLE`
		`Arc: TRANSFORM <dbl_cov> <sgl_cov>`

Use these guidelines when changing coordinate precision.

The following example shows how to convert a double-precision coverage to single precision while maintaining coordinate accuracy. A new coverage named SGLCOV is transformed from an input coverage named DBLCOV. DBLCOV is stored in State Plane feet and requires that 2,000,000 feet be subtracted from the x-coordinate to maintain accuracy. First create a new coverage in double precision using the existing coverage as a {tic_bnd_coverage}.

```
Arc: PRECISION
Usage: PRECISION <creation_rule> {processing_rule}
```

These PRECISION settings are the system defaults in ARC/INFO. The processing rule controls the precision of the created coverage.

```
Arc: PRECISION SINGLE DOUBLE
Arc: CREATE
Usage: CREATE <coverage> {tic_bnd_coverage}
Arc: CREATE NEWCOV DBLCOV
```

Next use INFO to subtract a constant value (i.e., 2,000,000) from the x-coordinate of each tic.

```
Arc: INFO
INFO 9.42 11/11/86 52.74.63*
Copyright (C) 1994 Doric Computer Systems
International, Ltd.
ENTER COMMAND> SELECT NEWCOV.TIC
ENTER COMMAND> CALC XTIC = XTIC - 2000000
ENTER COMMAND> Q STOP
```

Now copy NEWCOV, which is stored in double precision, to a single-precision coverage.

```
Arc: COPY NEWCOV SGLCOV SINGLE
```

Finally, use the TRANSFORM command to perform the translation.

```
Arc: TRANSFORM
Usage: TRANSFORM <from_cover> <to_cover>
                 {AFFINE | PROJECTIVE}
Arc: TRANSFORM DBLCOV SGLCOV
```

Layers have been translated so that their minimum x,y points are not the same. The TRANSFORM command can be used to shift in the x direction so that the coverages correctly overlap each other. Translations (x or y shifts) are often used to maintain accuracy in single-precision databases.

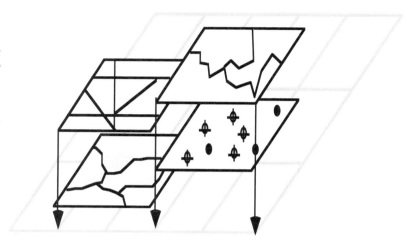

All layers correctly overlap. So the COPY command can be used to change precision. Keep in mind that copying double to single precision may cause loss of significant digits, and, therefore, loss of accuracy.

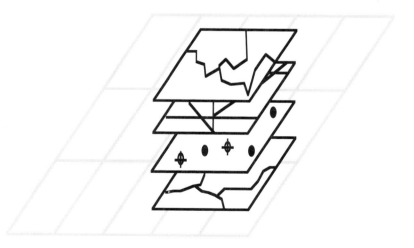

Enforcing coordinate compatibility

When combining spatial data, it is important to reference all input data to a common coordinate system. This holds true when combining tiles of a database, such as during edgematching, MAPJOIN or APPEND, and when overlaying data sets such as with UNION, CLIP, LATTICEMERGE, or the GET command in ARCEDIT.

Coordinate system information is stored with an ARC/INFO data set as a projection file (PRJ). The PROJECTCOMPARE command sets an environment that determines the degree of similarity required between projection files when combining data.

There are three levels at which the projection comparison can be set: NONE, PARTIAL, and FULL. Set to NONE, PROJECTCOMPARE makes no comparison of projection files. Any combinations of projection information will result in a match. Set to PARTIAL, one projection file must be defined, the other can be unknown, and will result in a match. Set to FULL, all projection information must be specified and identical in the projection file of each input data set.

```
PROJECTCOMPARE                       NONE    PARTIAL   FULL
UNKNOWN  / UNKNOWN                    MATCH   MATCH     NO MATCH
UNKNOWN  / PROJECTION A               MATCH   MATCH     NO MATCH
PROJECTION A / PROJECTION A           MATCH   MATCH     MATCH
PROJECTION A / PROJECTION B           MATCH   NO MATCH  NO MATCH
```

Similar projections and parameters which are defined in different ways will return a NO MATCH. For example, UNITS METERS and UNITS 1 (which are equal) will not match. Defining UTM and STATEPLANE projections by their central meridians or parallels will not match with the same projection if defined using the ZONES option.

Supported map projections

A total of forty-six map projections are available in the ARC/INFO environment at Version 7. A descriptive summary of each option is provided in this section. To make them easy to access, they are listed in alphabetical order, and each description follows the same format.

At the end of each description is a listing of subcommands and parameters prompts used to define that particular projection.

ALASKA_E	Alaska Series E.
ALASKA_GRID	Modified-Stereographic Conformal for Alaska.
ALBERS	Albers Conic Equal-Area.
AZIMUTHAL	Azimuthal Equidistant, Zenithal Equidistant.
BIPOLAR_ OBLIQUE	Bipolar Oblique Conic Conformal.
BONNE	Bonne.
CASSINI	Cassini-Soldner.
CHAMBERLIN	Chamberlin Trimetric.
CRASTER_ PARABOLIC	Craster Parabolic, Putnins P4.
CYLINDRICAL	Cylindrical Equal-Area, Lambert Cylindrical Equal-Area.
ECKERTIV	Eckert IV.
ECKERTVI	Eckert VI.
EQUIDISTANT	Equidistant Conic, Simple Conic, or Conic.

EQUI-RECTANGULAR	Simple Cylindrical, Equidistant Cylindrical, Rectangular or Plate Carrée.
FLAT_POLAR_QUARTIC	McBryde-Thomas Flat-Polar Quartic.
GALL_STEREO-GRAPHIC	Gall's Stereographic.
GEOCENTRIC	3-D Geocentric.
GEOGRAPHIC	Geographic Reference System, Global Reference System, GRS, or the Spherical Coordinate System.
GNOMONIC	Gnomonic, Gnomic.
GREATBRITAIN_GRID	Great Britain National Grid.
GRINTEN	Van der Grinten I.
HAMMER_AITOFF	Hammer-Aitoff.
LAMBERT	Lambert Conformal Conic.
LAMBERT_AZIMUTH	Lambert Azimuthal Equal-Area, Zenithal Equal-Area.
LOCAL	Local Cartesian Coordinate System.
MERCATOR	Mercator.
MILLER	Miller Cylindrical.
MOLLWEIDE	Mollweide, Babinet, Elliptical, Homolographic, and Homalographic.
NEWZEALAND_GRID	New Zealand National Grid.
OBLIQUE_MERCATOR	Oblique Mercator or Oblique Cylindrical Orthomorphic.
ORTHO-GRAPHIC	Orthographic.
PERSPECTIVE	Vertical Near-Side Perspective, Vertical Perspective.
POLAR	Universal Polar Stereographic, UPS, or Polar Stereographic.
POLYCONIC	Polyconic.
ROBINSON	Robinson or Orthophanic.

RSO	Rectified Skewed Orthomorphic.
SIMPLE_CONIC	Simple Conic, Equidistant Conic, or Conic.
SINUSOIDAL	Sinusoidal, Sanson-Flamsteed.
SPACE_ OBLIQUE_ MERCATOR	Space Oblique Mercator.
STATEPLANE	State Plane Coordinate System, SPCS.
STEREO- GRAPHIC	Stereographic.
TIMES	Bartholomew Times.
TRANSVERSE	Transverse Mercator.
TWO_POINT_ EQUIDISTANT	Two-point Equidistant.
UPS	Universal Polar Stereographic.
UTM	Universal Transverse Mercator.

ALASKA_E

Alaska Series E, Modified Transverse Mercator

This projection was developed in 1972 by the USGS to publish a map of Alaska at 1:2,500,000.

Method of projection

Approximates Equidistant Conic although it is commonly referred to as a 'Modified Transverse Mercator'.

Lines of secancy

The standard parallels at 53°30'N and 66°5'24"N.

Linear graticules

The meridians are straight lines radiating from a center point. The parallels closely approximate concentric circular arcs.

Properties

Shape

Neither conformal nor equal-area.

Area

Neither conformal nor equal-area.

Direction

Distortion increases with distance from the standard parallels.

Distance

Accurate along the standard parallels.

Limitations

This projection is appropriate for mapping Alaska, the Aleutian Islands, and the Bering Sea region only.

Uses & applications

■ 1972 USGS revision of a 1954 Alaska map which was published at 1:2,500,000.

■ 1974 map of the Aleutian Islands and the Bering Sea.

Projection definition

```
:PROJECTION ALASKA_E
:UNITS _____
:PARAMETERS
```

Projection-specific parameters are set by the software.

Subcommand usage

■ Units must be FEET, METERS, or units per meter.

ALASKA_GRID

Modified-Stereographic Conformal for Alaska

This projection was developed to provide a conformal map of Alaska with less scale distortion than other conformal projections. A set of mathematical formulas allows the definition of a conformal transformation between two surfaces (Snyder, 1987).

Method of projection

Modified planar. This is a sixth-order-equation modification of an oblique Stereographic conformal projection on the Clarke 1866 spheroid. The origin is at 64° N, 152° W.

Point of tangency

Conceptual point of tangency at 64° N, 152° W.

Linear graticules

None.

Properties

Shape

Perfectly conformal.

Area

Varies about 1.2% over Alaska.

Direction

Local angles are correct everywhere.

Distance

The minimum scale factor is 0.997 at approximately 62.5° N, 156° W. Scale increases outward from this point. Most of Alaska and the Aleutian Islands, but excluding the panhandle, is bounded by a line of true scale. The scale factor ranges from 0.997 to 1.003 for Alaska, which is one-fourth the range for a corresponding conic projection (Snyder, 1987).

Limitations

Distortion becomes severe away from Alaska.

Uses & applications

■ Conformal mapping of Alaska as a complete state.

Projection definition

```
:PROJECTION ALASKA_GRID
:UNITS _____
:PARAMETERS
```

Projection-specific parameters are set by the software.

Subcommand usage

■ Units must be FEET, METERS, or units per meter.

■ May also be specified by ALASKAN_GRID.

ALBERS

Albers Conic Equal-Area

This conic projection uses two standard parallels to reduce some of the distortion produced when only one standard parallel is used. Although neither shape nor linear scale are truly correct, the distortion of these properties is minimized in the region between the standard parallels. This projection is best suited for land masses that extend more in the east-to-west orientation than those lying north to south.

Method of projection

Conic. In this projection, the meridians are equally spaced straight lines converging at a common point. Poles are represented as arcs rather than as single points. Parallels are unequally spaced concentric circles, whose spacing decreases toward the poles.

Lines of secancy

Two lines, the standard parallels defined by degrees latitude.

Linear graticules

All meridians.

Properties

Shape

Shape along the standard parallels is accurate and minimally distorted in the region between the standard parallels and those regions just beyond. The 90-degree angles between meridians and parallels are preserved, but because the scale along the lines of longitude does not match the scale along lines of latitude, the final projection is *not* conformal.

Area

All areas are proportional to the same areas on the Earth.

Direction

Locally true along the standard parallels.

Distance

Projection distances are best in the middle latitudes. Along parallels, scale is reduced between the standard parallels and increased beyond them. Along meridians, scale follows an opposite pattern.

Limitations

Best results for regions predominantly east-west in extent and located in the middle latitudes. Total range in latitude from north to south should not exceed 30–35 degrees. No limitations on east to west range.

Uses & applications

■ Used for small regions or countries, but not for continents.

■ Coterminous United States, normally using 29° 30' and 45° 30' as the two standard parallels. For this projection, the maximum scale distortion for the 48 states is 1.25 percent.

■ Recommended choice of standard parallels can be calculated by determining the range in latitude from degrees north to south and dividing this range by six. Using the 'One-Sixth Rule' to determine standard parallels means that the 1st standard parallel is the southern boundary plus one-sixth the range and the 2nd standard parallel the northern limit minus one-sixth the range. There are also other possible approaches.

Projection definition

```
:PROJECTION ALBERS
:UNITS _____
:PARAMETERS
1st standard parallel:
2nd standard parallel:
Central meridian:
Latitude of projections origin:
False easting (meters):
False northing (meters):
```

Subcommand usage

■ Units must be FEET, METERS, or units per meter.

■ Degrees must be entered as DD MM SS. Values of longitude west of the Prime Meridian and of latitude south of the Equator are negative.

■ False easting and northing are real numbers and can be zero.

AZIMUTHAL

Azimuthal Equidistant, Zenithal Equidistant

The most significant characteristic of this map projection is that both distance and direction are accurate from the central point. This projection can accommodate all aspects, equatorial, polar and oblique.

Method of projection

Planar. The world is projected onto a flat surface from any point on the globe. Although all aspects are possible, the one used most commonly is the polar aspect, in which all meridians and parallels are divided equally to maintain the equidistant property. Oblique aspects centered on a city are also common.

Point of tangency

A single point, usually the North Pole or the South Pole, defined by degrees of latitude and longitude.

Linear graticules

Polar - Straight meridians are divided equally by concentric circles of latitude.

Equatorial - The Equator and the projection's central meridian are linear and meet at 90 degrees.

Oblique - The central meridian is straight but there are no 90-degree intersections except along the central meridian.

Properties

Shape

Except at the center, all shapes are distorted. Distortion increases from the center.

Area

Distortion increases outward from the center point.

Direction

True directions from the center outward.

Distance

Distances for all aspects are accurate from the center point outward. For the polar aspect, the distances along the meridians are accurate but there is a pattern of increasing distortion along the circles of latitude, outward from the center.

Limitations

Usually limited to 90 degrees from the center, although it can project the entire globe. Polar-aspect projections are best for regions within a 30-degree radius because there is only minimal distortion (Roblin).

Degrees from center	15	30	45	60	90
Percent scale distortion along parallels	1.2	4.7	11.1	20.9	57

Uses & applications

■ Routes of air and sea navigation. These maps will focus on an important location as their central point and use an appropriate aspect:

Polar aspect - Descriptive polar regions and polar navigation.

Equatorial aspect - Locations on or near the Equator, such as Singapore.

Oblique aspect - Locations between the poles and the Equator, such as large-scale mapping of Micronesia.

■ If this projection is used on the entire globe, the immediate hemisphere can be recognized and resembles the LAMBERT_AZIMUTH projection. The outer hemisphere greatly distorts shapes and areas. In the extreme, a polar-aspect projection centered on the North Pole will represent the South Pole as its largest outermost circle. The function of this extreme projection is that, regardless of the conformal and area distortion, an accurate presentation of distance and direction from the center point is maintained.

Projection definition

```
:PROJECTION AZIMUTHAL
:UNITS _____
:PARAMETERS
Radius of the sphere of reference:
Longitude of center of projection:
Latitude of center of projection:
False easting (meters):
False northing (meters):
```

Subcommand usage

■ Units must be FEET, METERS, or units per meter.

■ The radius of the sphere of reference is a real number. A zero can be entered to indicate the default radius: 6,370,997 meters.

■ This projection is supported only on a sphere. For information on using this projection with a datum or spheroid, refer to 'Projections on a sphere' in Appendix B of this book.

■ Degrees must be entered as DD MM SS. Values of longitude west of the Prime Meridian and of latitude south of the Equator are negative.

■ False easting and northing are real numbers and can be zero.

BIPOLAR_OBLIQUE

Bipolar Oblique Conic Conformal

This projection was developed specifically for mapping North and South America. It maintains conformality for North and South America. It is based upon the Lambert Conformal Conic, using two oblique conic projections side by side.

Method of projection

Two oblique conics are joined with the poles 104° apart. A great circle arc 104° long begins at 20° S and 110° W, cuts through Central America, and terminates at 45° N and approximately 19°59'36" W. The scale of the map is then increased by approximately 3.5 percent. The origin of the coordinates is made 17°15' N, 73°02' W (Snyder, 1987).

Lines of secancy

Two oblique cones are conceptually secant along two lines each. These standard lines do not follow any single parallel or meridian.

Linear graticules

Only from each transformed pole to the nearest actual pole.

Properties

Shape

Conformality is maintained except for a slight discrepancy at the juncture of the two conic projections.

Area

Minimal distortion near the standard lines, increasing with distance from them.

Direction

Local directions are accurate because of conformality.

Distance

True along standard lines.

Limitations

Specialized for displaying North and South America together.

Uses & applications

■ Developed in 1941 by the American Geographical Society as a low-error single map of North and South America.

■ Conformal mapping of North and South America as a contiguous unit.

■ Used by USGS for geologic mapping of North America until replaced in 1979 by the Transverse Mercator.

Projection definition

```
:PROJECTION BIPOLAR_OBLIQUE
:UNITS  _____
:PARAMETERS
```

Projection-specific parameters are set by the software.

Subcommand usage

■ Units must be FEET, METERS, or units per meter.

■ This projection is supported only on a sphere. For information on using this projection with a datum or spheroid, refer to 'Projections on a sphere' in Appendix B of this book.

■ May also be specified by BIPOLAR.

BONNE

Bonne

This equal-area projection has true scale along the central meridian and all parallels.

Method of projection

Pseudoconic. Parallels of latitude are equally spaced concentric circular arcs, marked true to scale for meridians.

Point of tangency

A single standard parallel with no distortion.

Linear graticules

The central meridian.

Properties

Shape

No distortion along the central meridian and standard parallel; error increases away from these lines.

Area

Equal area.

Direction

Locally true along central meridian and standard parallel.

Distance

Scale is true along the central meridian and along each parallel.

Limitations

Usually limited to maps of continents or smaller regions. Distortion pattern makes other equal-area projections preferable.

Uses & applications

■ During the 19th and early 20th century for atlas maps of Asia, Australia, Europe, and North America. Replaced by the Lambert Azimuthal Equal-Area for continental mapping by Rand McNally & Co. and Hammond, Inc.

■ Large-scale topographic mapping of France and Ireland, along with Morocco and some other Mediterranean countries (Snyder, 1987).

Projection definition

```
:PROJECTION BONNE
:UNITS _____
:PARAMETERS
Longitude of projection center:
Latitude of projection center:
False easting (meters):
False northing (meters):
```

Subcommand usage

■ Units must be FEET, METERS or units per meter.

■ Degrees must be entered as DD MM SS. Values of longitude west of the Prime Meridian and of latitude south of the Equator are negative.

■ False easting and northing are real numbers and can be zero.

■ Equatorial aspect is a Sinusoidal. Polar aspect is a Werner.

CASSINI

Cassini, Cassini-Soldner

This transverse cylindrical projection maintains scale along the central meridian and all lines parallel to it, and is neither equal-area nor conformal. It is most suited for large-scale mapping of areas with predominantly north-south in extent.

Method of projection

A transverse cylinder is conceptually projected onto the globe, and is tangent along the central meridian. Cassini is analogous to the Equirectangular projection in the same way the Transverse Mercator is to Mercator projection. The name Cassini-Soldner refers to the more accurate ellipsoidal version developed in the 19th Century, used in this software.

Point of tangency

Conceptually a line, specified as the central meridian.

Linear graticules

The Equator, central meridian, and each meridian 90 degrees from the central meridian.

Properties

Shape

No distortion along the central meridian. Distortion increases with distance from the central meridian.

Area

No distortion along the central meridian. Distortion increases with distance from the central meridian.

Direction

Generally distorted.

Distance

Scale distortion increases with distance from the central meridian, however, scale is accurate along the central meridian and all lines perpendicular to the central meridian.

Limitations

Should be used primarily for large-scale mapping of areas near the central meridian. Transverse Mercator often preferred because of difficulty measuring scale and direction on Cassini.

Uses & applications

■ Normally used for large-scale maps of areas predominantly north-south in extent.

■ Used for the Ordnance Survey of Great Britain, and some German states in the late 19th century. Also used in Cyprus,

former Czechoslovakia, Denmark, Malaysia, and the former
Federal Republic of Germany.

Projection definition

```
:PROJECTION CASSINI
:UNITS _____
:PARAMETERS
Longitude of projection center:
Latitude of projection center:
False easting (meters):
False northing (meters):
```

Subcommand usage

■ Units must be FEET, METERS, or units per meter.

■ Degrees must be entered as DD MM SS. Values of longitude
west of the Prime Meridian and of latitude south of the Equator are
negative.

CHAMBERLIN

Chamberlin Trimetric

This is the standard projection developed and used by the National Geographic Society for continental mapping. The distance from three input points to any other point is approximately correct.

Method of projection

Modified planar.

Linear graticules

None.

Properties

Shape

Shape distortion is low throughout if the three points are placed near the map limits.

Area

Areal distortion is low throughout if the three points are placed near the map limits.

Direction

Low distortion throughout.

Distance

Nearly correct representation of distance from three widely spaced points to any other point.

Limitations

The three selected input points should be widely spaced near the edge of the map limits.

Chamberlin can only be used in ARC/INFO as an OUTPUT projection, and therefore cannot be used to project an ARC/INFO grid or lattice.

Uses & applications

■ Used by the National Geographic Society as the standard map projection for most continents.

Projection definition

```
:PROJECTION CHAMBERLIN
:UNITS _____
:PARAMETERS
Longitude of point A:
Latitude of point A:
Longitude of point B:
Latitude of point B:
Longitude of point C:
Latitude of point C:
```

Subcommand usage

■ Units must be entered as FEET, METERS, or units per meter.

■ Degrees must be entered as DD MM SS. Values of longitude west of the Prime Meridian and of latitude south of the Equator are negative.

■ This projection is supported only on a sphere. For information on using this projection with a datum or spheroid, refer to 'Projections on a sphere' in Appendix B of this book.

CRASTER_PARABOLIC

Craster Parabolic, Putnins P₄

This pseudocylindrical equal-area projection is primarily used for thematic maps of the world.

Method of projection

Pseudocylindrical.

Linear graticules

The central meridian is a straight line half as long as the Equator. Parallels are unequally spaced, straight parallel lines perpendicular to the central meridian. Their spacing changes very gradually, and they are farthest apart near the Equator.

Properties

Shape

Free of distortion along the central meridian at 36°46' N and S. Distortion increases with distance from these points and is most severe at the outer meridians and high latitudes. This distortion can be greatly reduced by interrupting the projection.

Area

Equal-area.

Direction

Local angles are correct at the intersection of 36°46' N and S with the central meridian. Direction is distorted elsewhere.

Distance

Scale is true along latitudes 36°46' N and S. Scale is also constant along any given latitude, and the same for the latitude of opposite sign.

Limitations

Useful only as a world map.

Uses & applications

- Thematic world maps.

Projection definition

```
:PROJECTION CRASTER_PARABOLIC
:UNITS _____
:PARAMETERS
Longitude of central meridian:
```

Subcommand usage

- Units must be FEET, METERS, or units per meter.

- Degrees must be entered as DD MM SS. Values of longitude west of the Prime Meridian and of latitude south of the Equator are negative.

- This projection is supported only on a sphere. For information on using this projection with a datum or spheroid, refer to 'Projections on a sphere' in Appendix B of this book.

CYLINDRICAL

Cylindrical Equal-Area, Lambert Cylindrical Equal-Area

Method of projection

Cylindrical. Type 1 is a normal, perspective projection onto a cylinder tangent at the Equator. Type 2 and Type 3 are oblique aspects, from which normal and transverse aspects are also possible.

Points of intersection

Type 1 is tangent at the Equator. Type 2 can be tangent or secant. Type 3 is tangent.

Linear graticules

Type 1

In the normal, or equatorial aspect, all meridians and parallels are straight lines at right angles to each other. Meridians are equally spaced and 0.32 times the length of the Equator. Parallels are unequally spaced, and farthest apart near the Equator. Poles are lines of length equal to the Equator.

Types 2 & 3

In a transverse aspect, the Equator along with the central meridian and a meridian perpendicular to the Equator are straight lines. In an oblique aspect, only two meridians are straight lines.

Properties

Shape

Shape is true along the standard parallels of the normal aspect (Type 1), or the standard lines of the transverse and oblique aspects (Types 2 and 3). Shape distortion is severe near the poles of the normal aspect or 90° from the central line in the transverse and oblique aspects.

Area

There is no distortion of area on any of the projections.

Direction

Local angles are correct along standard parallels or standard lines. Direction is distorted elsewhere.

Distance

Scale is true along the Equator (Type 1), or the standard lines of the transverse and oblique aspects (Types 2 and 3). Scale distortion is severe near the poles of the normal aspect or 90° from the central line in the transverse and oblique aspects.

Limitations

Recommended for narrow areas extending along the central line. Severe distortion of shape and scale near poles of Type 1, and 90° from the central line of the transverse and oblique aspects.

Uses & applications

■ Type 1 is suitable for equatorial regions.

■ Suitable for regions of north-south extent or those following an oblique central line when using a transverse or oblique view, respectively.

Projection definition

```
:PROJECTION CYLINDRICAL
:UNITS _____
:PARAMETERS
Enter projection type (1,2, or 3):
```

Type 1 parameters

```
Longitude of central meridian:
Latitude of standard parallel:
```

Type 2 parameters

```
Longitude of 1st point:
Latitude of 1st point:
Longitude of 2nd point:
Latitude of 2nd point:
Scale factor:
```

Type 3 parameters

```
Longitude of center of projection:
Latitude of center of projection:
Azimuth:
Scale factor:
```

Subcommand usage

■ Units must be FEET, METERS or units per meter.

■ Degrees must be entered in DD MM SS. Values of longitude west of the Prime Meridian and of latitude south of the Equator are negative.

■ Azimuth must be entered as an angle in decimal degrees.

■ Scale factor of the central line is a real number, usually one.

■ This projection is supported only on a sphere. For information on using this projection with a datum or spheroid, refer to 'Projections on a sphere' in Appendix B of this book.

ECKERTIV

Eckert IV

This equal-area projection is used primarily for world maps.

Method of projection

A pseudocylindrical, equal-area projection, on which all parallels are straight lines and all meridians are equally spaced elliptical arcs, except the central meridian, which is a straight line.

Linear graticules

All parallels are unequally spaced straight lines, closer together at the poles. The poles and the central meridian are straight lines half as long as the Equator.

Properties

Shape

Shapes are stretched north-south 40 percent along the Equator, relative to the east-west dimension. This stretching decreases to zero at 40°30' N and S at the central meridian. Nearer the poles, features are compressed in the north-south direction.

Area

Equivalent.

Direction

Local angles are correct at the intersection of 40°30' N and S with the central meridian. Direction is distorted elsewhere.

Distance

Scale is distorted north-south 40 percent along the Equator relative to the east-west dimension. This distortion decreases to zero at 40°30' N and S at the central meridian. Scale is correct only along these parallels. Nearer the poles, features are compressed in the north-south direction.

Limitations

Useful only as a world map.

Uses & applications

- Thematic maps of the world, such as climate.

Projection definition

```
:PROJECTION ECKERTIV
:UNITS _____
:PARAMETERS
Longitude of central meridian:
```

Subcommand usage

- Units must be FEET, METERS, or units per meter.

- Degrees must be entered in DD MM SS. Values of longitude west of the Prime Meridian and of latitude south of the Equator are negative.

■ This projection is supported only on a sphere. For information on using this projection with a datum or spheroid, refer to 'Projections on a sphere' in Appendix B of this book.

■ May be specified by ECKERTIV or ECKERT4.

ECKERTVI

Eckert VI

This equal-area projection is used primarily for world maps.

Method of projection

A pseudocylindrical, equal-area projection, where all parallels are straight lines and all meridians are equally spaced sinusoidal curves, except the central meridian, which is a straight line.

Linear graticules

All parallels are unequally spaced straight lines, closer together at the poles. The poles and the central meridian are straight lines half as long as the Equator.

Properties

Shape

Shapes are stretched north-south 29 percent along the Equator, relative to the east-west dimension. This stretching decreases to zero at 49°16' N and S at the central meridian. Nearer the poles, features are compressed in the north-south direction.

Area

Equivalent.

Direction

Local angles are correct at the intersection of 49°16' N and S with the central meridian. Direction is distorted elsewhere.

Distance

Scale is distorted north-south 29 percent along the Equator relative to the east-west dimension. This distortion decreases to zero at 49°16' N and S at the central meridian. Scale is correct only along these parallels. Nearer the poles, features are compressed in the north-south direction.

Limitations

Useful only as a world map.

Uses & applications

■ Suitable for thematic mapping of the world.

■ World distribution maps in the 1937 World Atlas by the Soviet Union.

Projection definition

```
:PROJECTION ECKERTVI
:UNITS _____
:PARAMETERS
Longitude of central meridian:
```

Subcommand usage

■ Units must be FEET, METERS, or units per meter.

■ Degrees must be entered in DD MM SS. Values of longitude west of the Prime Meridian and of latitude south of the Equator are negative.

■ This projection is supported only on a sphere. For information on using this projection with a datum or spheroid, refer to 'Projections on a sphere' in Appendix B of this book.

■ May be specified as ECKERTVI or ECKERT6.

EQUIDISTANT

Equidistant Conic, Simple Conic, or Conic

This conic projection can be based on one or two standard parallels. As the name implies, all circular parallels are an equal distance from each other, spaced evenly along the meridians. This is true whether one or two parallels are used as the standards.

Method of projection

Cone is tangential if only one standard parallel is specified and secant for two standard parallels. Graticules are evenly spaced. The space between each meridian is equal, as is the space between each of the concentric arcs that describe the lines of latitude. The poles are represented as arcs rather than points.

Lines of contact

Depends on the number of standard parallels.

Tangential projections (Type 1) - One line, indicated by the standard parallel.

Secant projections (Type 2) - Two lines, specified as 1st and 2nd standard parallels.

Linear graticules

All meridians.

Properties

Shape

Local shapes are true along the standard parallels. Distortion is constant along any given parallel. Distortion increases with distance from the standard parallels.

Area

Distortion is constant along any given parallel. Distortion increases with distance from the standard parallels.

Direction

Locally true along the standard parallels.

Distance

True along the meridians and the standard parallels. Scale is constant along any given parallel, but changes from parallel to parallel.

Limitations

Range in latitude should be limited to 30 degrees.

Uses & applications

■ Regional mapping of mid-latitude areas with a predominantly east-west expanse.

■ Common for atlas maps of small countries.

■ Used by the Soviet Union for mapping the entire country.

Projection definition

```
:PROJECTION EQUIDISTANT
:UNITS _____
:PARAMETERS
Number of standard parallels < 1 | 2 >:
```

Type 1

```
Longitude of the central meridian (DMS):
Latitude of the origin (DMS):
Latitude of the standard parallel (DMS):
```

Type 2

```
Longitude of the central meridian (DMS):
Latitude of the origin (DMS):
Latitude of the 1st standard parallel (DMS):
Latitude of the 2nd standard parallel (DMS):
```

Subcommand usage

■ Units must be FEET, METERS, or units per meter.

■ Degrees must be entered as DD MM SS. Values of longitude west of the Prime Meridian and of latitude south of the Equator are negative.

■ If the pole is given as the single standard parallel, the cone becomes a plane and the resulting projection is the same as a polar Azimuthal Equidistant.

■ If two standard parallels are placed symmetrically north and south of the Equator, the resulting projection is the same as Equirectangular and the Equirectangular projection must be used.

■ If the standard parallel is the Equator, the Equirectangular projection must be used.

■ May also be specified by SIMPLE_CONIC.

EQUIRECTANGULAR

Simple Cylindrical, Equidistant Cylindrical, Rectangular or Plate Carrée

This projection is very simple to construct because it forms a grid of equal rectangles. Because of its simple calculations, its usage was more common in the past than it is today. The polar regions are less distorted in scale and area in this projection than they are with the Mercator projection.

Method of projection

This simple cylindrical projection converts the globe into a Cartesian grid. Each rectangular grid cell has the same size, shape and area. All the graticular intersections are 90 degrees. The central parallel may be any line, but the traditional Plate Carrée projection uses the Equator. When the Equator is used, the grid cells are perfect squares, but if any other parallel is used, the grids become rectangular. In this projection, the poles are represented as straight lines across the top and bottom.

Lines of contact

Tangent at the Equator, or secant at two parallels symmetrical about the Equator.

Linear graticules

All meridians and all parallels.

Properties

Shape

Distortion increases as the distance from the standard parallels increases.

Area

Distortion increases as the distance from the standard parallels increases.

Direction

Following the grid lines are accurate directions: due east, west, south and north. General directions are distorted, except locally along the standard parallels.

Distance

The scale is correct along all the meridians and along the standard parallels.

Limitations

Noticeable distortion away from standard parallels.

Uses & applications

■ Best used for city maps, or other small areas with map scales small enough to reduce the obvious distortion.

■ Used for simple portrayals of the world or regions with minimal geographic data, such as index maps.

Projection definition

```
:PROJECTION EQUIRECTANGULAR
:UNITS _____
:PARAMETERS
Radius of the sphere of reference:
Longitude of central meridian:
Latitude of standard parallel:
False easting (meters):
False northing (meters):
```

Subcommand usage

■ Units must be FEET, METERS, or units per meter.

■ The radius of the sphere of reference is a real number. A zero can be entered to indicate the default radius: 6,370,997 meters.

■ This projection is supported only on a sphere. For information on using this projection with a datum or spheroid, refer to 'Projections on a sphere' in Appendix B of this book.

■ Degrees must be entered as DD MM SS. Values of longitude west of the Prime Meridian and of latitude south of the Equator are negative.

■ False easting and northing are real numbers and can be zero.

FLAT_POLAR_QUARTIC

McBryde-Thomas Flat-Polar Quartic

This equal-area projection is primarily used for world maps.

Method of projection

A pseudocylindrical, equal-area projection in which all parallels are straight lines, and all meridians except the straight central meridian are equally spaced, fourth-order (quartic) curves.

Linear graticules

All parallels are unequally spaced straight lines, closer together at the poles. The poles are straight lines one-third as long as the Equator. The central meridian is a straight line 0.45 times as long as the Equator.

Properties

Shape

Shapes are stretched north-south along the Equator, relative to the east-west dimension. This stretching decreases to zero at 33°45' N and S at the central meridian. Nearer the poles, features are compressed in the north-south direction.

Area

Equal-area.

Direction

Distorted except at the intersection of 33°45' N and S and the central meridian.

Distance

Scale is distorted everywhere except along 33°45' N and S.

Limitations

Useful only as a world map.

Uses & applications

■ Thematic maps of the world.

Projection definition

```
:PROJECTION FLAT_POLAR_QUARTIC
:UNITS _____
:PARAMETERS
Longitude of projection's center:
```

Subcommand usage

■ Units must be FEET, METERS, or units per meter.

■ Degrees must be entered as DD MM SS. Values of longitude west of the Prime Meridian and of latitude south of the Equator are negative.

■ This projection is supported only on a sphere. For information on using this projection with a datum or spheroid, refer to 'Projections on a sphere' in Appendix B of this book.

GALL_STEREOGRAPHIC

Gall's Stereographic

Gall's Stereographic is a cylindrical projection designed around 1855 with two standard parallels at latitudes 45˚N and 45˚S.

Method of projection

Cylindrical stereographic projection based upon two standard parallels at 45° N and S. The globe is projected perspectively onto a secant cylinder from the point on the Equator opposite a given meridian. Meridians are equally spaced straight lines. Parallels are straight lines closer together near the Equator. Poles are straight lines.

Lines of secancy

Two lines at 45° N and S.

Linear graticules

All meridians and parallels.

Properties

Shape

Shape is true at latitudes 45° N and S. Distortion increases slowly from these latitudes and becomes severe at the poles.

Area

Area is true at latitudes 45° N and S. Distortion increases slowly from these latitudes and becomes severe at the poles.

Direction

Locally correct at latitudes 45° N and S. Generally distorted elsewhere.

Distance

Scale is true in all directions along latitudes 45° N and S. Scale is constant along any other given latitude or its opposite. Distances are compressed between latitudes 45° N and S, and expanded beyond them.

Limitations

Used only for world maps.

Uses & applications

■ World maps in British atlases.

Projection definition

```
:PROJECTION GALL_STEREOGRAPHIC
:UNITS _____
:PARAMETERS
Longitude of central meridian:
```

Subcommand usage

■ Units must be FEET, METERS, or units per meter.

■ Degrees must be entered in DD MM SS. Values of longitude west of the Prime Meridian and of latitude south of the Equator are negative.

■ This projection is supported only on a sphere. For information on using this projection with a datum or spheroid, refer to 'Projections on a sphere' in Appendix B of this book.

■ May also be specified as GALLS_STEREOGRAPHIC.

GEOCENTRIC

3-D Geocentric

Although an option in the PROJECT command, this is not truly a map projection, since it works in a three-dimensional coordinate system. GEOCENTRIC converts longitude-latitude coordinate pairs into x,y,z values based on an ellipsoidal earth. These values are in a rectangular coordinate system with linear units.

Uses & applications

■ Primarily used in surveying and land records management applications.

Projection definition

```
:PROJECTION GEOCENTRIC
:UNITS _____
:PARAMETERS
```

Projection-specific parameters are set by the software.

Subcommand usage

■ Units must be FEET, METERS, or units per meter.

■ This projection can only be used with the FILE option, since the output contains a z-value.

GEOGRAPHIC

Geographic Reference System, Global Reference System, GRS, or the Spherical Coordinate System

Although GEOGRAPHIC is an option within the PROJECT command, it is not a map projection. The Geographic Reference System consists of latitude and longitude. This system treats the globe as if it were a sphere or spheroid. The sphere is divided into 360 equal parts called degrees. Each degree can be further subdivided into 60 minutes, each composed of 60 seconds. The standard origin is where the Greenwich Prime Meridian meets the Equator. All points north of the Equator and east of the Prime Meridian are positive. The origin divides the globe into four quadrants: northwest, northeast, southwest and southeast. Each line of longitude runs north and south and measures the number of degrees east or west of the Prime Meridian. Values range from positive 180 to negative 180 degrees. Lines of latitude run from east to west and measure the number of degrees north or south of the Equator. Values range from the North Pole, at positive 90 degrees, to the South Pole which is located at negative 90 degrees. (See the diagram of the Spherical Coordinate System on page 2-8.)

Uses & applications

■ Values of latitude and longitude are used in all the other options to reference such parameters as the central meridian, the latitude of the true scale and the center of the projection as specified by latitude and longitude.

Projection definition

```
:PROJECTION GEOGRAPHIC
:UNITS __
:QUADRANT __
:PARAMETERS
```

Subcommand usage

■ Units must be DD, DM, DS or DMS. DMS can only be used when projecting an ASCII file of coordinates.

■ Quadrant specification is optional and can be NE, NW, SW or SE.

■ There are *no* parameter specifications.

GNOMONIC

Gnomonic, Gnomic

This azimuthal projection uses the center of the Earth as its perspective point. All great circles are straight lines, regardless of the aspect. This is a useful projection for routes of navigation because the great circles highlight routes with the shortest distance.

Method of projection

This is a planar perspective projection, viewed from the center of the globe. The projection can be any aspect.

Point of tangency

A single point anywhere on the globe.

Polar aspect - North Pole or South Pole.

Equatorial aspect - Any point along the Equator.

Oblique aspect - Any other point.

Linear graticules

All meridians and the Equator.

Properties

Shape

Increasingly distorted from the center; moderate distortion within 30 degrees of the center point.

Area

Distortion increases with distance from the center; moderate distortion within a 30-degree radius of the center.

Direction

Accurate from the center.

Distance

No line has an accurate scale, and the amount of distortion increases with distance from the center.

Scalar distortion for Polar Aspect				
Degrees from Center	15.0	30.0	45.0	60.0
Meridian Distortion (%)	7.2	33.3	100.0	300.0
Latitude Distortion (%)	3.5	15.5	41.4	100.0

Limitations

This projection is limited by its perspective point and cannot project a line that is 90 degrees or more from the center point; this means that the equatorial aspect cannot project the poles, and the polar aspects cannot project the Equator.

A radius of 30 degrees produces moderate distortion, as indicated in the table above. This projection should not be used more than about 60 degrees from the center.

Uses & applications

■ All aspects - Routes of navigation for sea and air.

■ Polar aspect - Navigational maps of polar regions.

■ Equatorial aspect - Navigational maps of Africa and the tropical region of South America.

Projection definition

```
:PROJECTION GNOMONIC
:UNITS _____
:PARAMETERS
Radius of the sphere of reference:
Longitude of center of projection:
Latitude of center of projection:
False easting (meters):
False northing (meters):
```

Subcommand usage

■ Units must be FEET, METERS, or units per meter.

■ The radius of the sphere of reference is a real number. A zero can be entered to indicate the default radius: 6,370,997 meters.

■ This projection is supported only on a sphere. For information on using this projection with a datum or spheroid, refer to 'Projections on a sphere' in Appendix B of this book.

■ Degrees must be entered as DD MM SS. Values of longitude west of the Prime Meridian and of latitude south of the Equator are negative.

■ False easting and northing are real numbers, and can be zero.

GREATBRITAIN_GRID

Great Britain National Grid

This is a Transverse Mercator projected on the Airy spheroid. The central meridian is scaled to 0.9996. The origin is 49° N and 2° W.

Method of projection

Cylindrical, transverse projection with the central meridian centered along a particular region.

Lines of secancy

Two lines parallel with and 180 km from the central meridian at 2° W.

Linear graticules

The central meridian.

Properties

Shape

Conformal, therefore, small shapes are maintained accurately.

Area

Distortion increases beyond Great Britain as the distance from the central meridian increases.

Direction

Local directions are accurately maintained.

Distance

Scale is accurate along the lines of secancy 180 km from the central meridian. Scale is compressed between them and expanded beyond them.

Limitations

Suitable for Great Britain. Limited in east-west extent.

Uses & applications

■ The national projection for Great Britain, used for large-scale topographic mapping.

Projection definition

```
:PROJECTION GREATBRITAIN_GRID
:UNITS _____
:PARAMETERS
```

Projection-specific parameters are set by the software.

Subcommand usage

■ Units must be FEET, METERS, or units per meter.

GRINTEN

Van der Grinten I

This projection is similar to the Mercator projection except that it portrays the world as a circle, with a curved graticule. The overall effect is that area is distorted less than on the Mercator, and the shape is distorted less than on equal-area projections.

Method of projection

A compromise projection, not in one of the more traditional classifications.

Linear graticules

The Equator and the central meridian of the projection.

Properties

Shape

Distortion increases from the Equator to the poles.

Area

Minimal distortion along the Equator and extreme distortion in the polar regions.

Direction

Local angles are correct only at the center.

Distance

Scale along the Equator is correct.

Limitations

Can represent the world, but the best presentation is between the 75th parallels of latitude.

Uses & applications

■ World maps.

■ Formerly the standard world map projection of the National Geographic Society.

Projection definition

```
:PROJECTION GRINTEN
:UNITS _____
:PARAMETERS
Radius of the sphere of reference:
Longitude of central meridian:
False easting (meters):
False northing (meters):
```

Subcommand usage

■ Units must be FEET, METERS, or units per meter.

■ The radius of the sphere of reference is a real number. A zero can be entered to indicate the default radius: 6,370,997 meters.

■ This projection is supported only on a sphere. For information on using this projection with a datum or spheroid, refer to 'Projections on a sphere' in Appendix B of this book.

■ Degrees must be entered as DD MM SS. Values of longitude west of the Prime Meridian and of latitude south of the Equator are negative.

■ False easting and northing are real numbers and can be zero.

HAMMER_AITOFF

Hammer-Aitoff

Method of projection

Modified planar. In this modified azimuthal projection, the central meridian is a straight line half as long as the Equator. The other meridians are complex curves, concave toward the central meridian, and unequally spaced along the Equator. The Equator is a straight line, all other parallels are complex curves, concave toward the nearest pole, and unequally spaced along the central meridian.

Point of tangency

Central meridian at the Equator.

Linear graticules

The Equator and central meridian are the only straight lines.

Properties

Shape

Distortion increases away from the origin.

Area

Equal-area.

Direction

Local angles are true only at the center.

Distance

Scale decreases along the Equator and central meridian as distance from the origin increases.

Limitations

Useful only as a world map.

Uses & applications

■ Thematic maps of the whole world.

Projection definition

```
:PROJECTION HAMMER_AITOFF
:UNITS _____
:PARAMETERS
Longitude of central meridian:
```

Subcommand usage

■ Units must be FEET, METERS, or units per meter.

■ The radius of the sphere of reference is a real number. A zero can be entered to indicate the default radius: 6,370,997 meters.

■ This projection is supported only on a sphere. For information on using this projection with a datum or spheroid, refer to 'Projections on a sphere' in Appendix B of this book.

■ Degrees must be entered as DD MM SS. Values of longitude west of the Prime Meridian and of latitude south of the Equator are negative.

LAMBERT

Lambert Conformal Conic

This projection is one of the best for middle latitudes. It is similar to the Albers Conic Equal-Area projection except that it portrays shape more accurately than area. The State Plane Coordinate System uses this projection for all state zones that spread east to west.

Method of projection

Conic projection normally based on two standard parallels, making it a secant projection. The spacing between lines of latitude increases beyond the standard parallels. This is the only common conic projection that represents the poles as a single point.

Lines of secancy

The two standard parallels.

Linear graticules

All meridians.

Properties

Shape

All graticular intersections are 90 degrees. Small shapes are maintained.

Area

Minimal distortion near the standard parallels. Areal scale is reduced between standard parallels and increased beyond them.

Direction

Local angles are accurate throughout because of conformality.

Distance

Correct scale along the standard parallels. The scale is reduced between the parallels and increased beyond the parallels.

Limitations

Best results are for regions predominantly east-west in extent and located in the middle north or south latitudes. Total range in latitude should not exceed 35 degrees.

Uses & applications

■ State Plane Coordinate System (SPCS), used for all east-west State Plane zones.

■ USGS 7 1/2-minute quad sheets to match the State Plane Coordinate System.

■ This projection was used for many new USGS maps after 1957. It replaced the previous Polyconic projection.

■ Continental U.S.: standard parallels, 33 and 45 degrees North.

■ Entire U.S.: standard parallels, 37 and 65 degrees North.

Projection definition

```
:PROJECTION LAMBERT
:UNITS  _____
:PARAMETERS
1st standard parallel:
2nd standard parallel:
Central meridian:
Latitude of projections origin:
False easting (meters):
False northing (meters):
```

Subcommand usage

- Units must be FEET, METERS, or units per meter.

- Degrees must be entered as DD MM SS. Values of longitude west of the Prime Meridian and of latitude south of the Equator are negative.

- False easting and northing are real numbers and can be zero.

- The latitude of origin defines the origin of the Y-coordinates for the projection.

LAMBERT_AZIMUTH

Lambert Azimuthal Equal-Area, Zenithal Equal-Area

This projection preserves the area of individual polygons while simultaneously maintaining a true sense of direction from the center. The general pattern of distortion is radial. This projection is best suited for individual land masses that are symmetrically proportioned, either round or square.

Method of projection

Planar, projected onto a flat surface from any point on the globe. This projection can accommodate all aspects: equatorial, polar, and oblique.

Point of tangency

A single point, located anywhere, specified by longitude and latitude. This point is the arithmetic center when the projection is shown as a hemisphere.

Linear graticules

All aspects - The central meridian defining the point of tangency.

Equatorial aspect - The Equator.

Polar aspect - All meridians.

Properties

Shape

Shape is minimally distorted, less than 2 percent, within 15 degrees from the focal point. Beyond that, angular distortion is more significant; small shapes are compressed radially from the center and elongated perpendicularly.

Area

Equal-area.

Direction

True direction radiating from the central point.

Distance

True at center. Scale decreases with distance from the center along radii and increases with increasing distance from the center perpendicular to the radii.

Limitations

The data must be less than a hemisphere in extent. The software cannot process any area more than 90 degrees from the central point in any direction.

Uses & applications

■ Population density (area).

■ Political boundaries (area).

■ Oceanic mapping for energy, minerals, geology and tectonics (direction).

■ This projection can handle large areas, thus it is used for displaying such geographical areas as entire continents and polar regions.

Equatorial aspect   - Africa, Southeast Asia, Australia, Caribbean and Central America

Oblique aspect   - North America, Europe and Asia

Projection definition

```
:PROJECTION LAMBERT_AZIMUTH
:UNITS _____
:PARAMETERS
Radius of sphere of reference:
Longitude of center of projection:
Latitude of center of projection:
False easting:
False northing:
```

Subcommand usage

■ Units must be FEET, METERS, or units per meter.

■ A zero can be used for the first parameter specification to indicate the default radius: 6,370,997 meters.

■ This projection is supported only on a sphere. For information on using this projection with a datum or spheroid, refer to 'Projections on a sphere' in Appendix B of this book.

■ Degrees must be entered as DD MM SS. Values of longitude west of the Prime Meridian and of latitude south of the Equator are negative.

■ False easting and northing are real numbers and can be zero.

LOCAL

Local Cartesian Coordinate System

This is a specialized map projection which does not take into account the curvature of the Earth. It is designed for very large-scale mapping applications.

Method of projections

The coordinates of the center of the area of interest define the origin of the local coordinate system. The plane is tangent to the spheroid at that point and the differences in z are negligible between corresponding points on the spheroid and the plane. Because the differences in z are ignored, distortions will greatly increase beyond roughly 1 degree from the origin.

Uses & applications

■ Large-scale mapping. Should not be used for areas of extent greater than 1 degree square.

Projection definition

```
:PROJECTION LOCAL
:UNITS _____
:PARAMETERS
Longitude of the origin:
Latitude of the origin:
```

Subcommand usage

■ Units must be FEET, METERS, or units per meter.

■ Degrees must be entered as DD MM SS. Values of longitude west of the Prime Meridian and of latitude south of the Equator are negative.

MERCATOR

Mercator

Originally created to display accurate compass bearings for those traveling on the seas. An additional feature of this projection is that all local shapes are accurate and clearly defined.

Method of projection

Cylindrical projection. Meridians are parallel to each other and are equally spaced. The lines of latitude are also parallel but become farther apart toward the poles. The poles cannot be shown.

Lines of contact

The Equator. May also be secant at two latitudes symmetrical about the Equator.

Linear graticules

All meridians and all lines of latitude.

Properties

Shape

Conformal. Small shapes are well represented because this projection maintains the local angular relationships.

Area

Increasingly distorted toward the polar regions. For example, in the Mercator projection of the world, Greenland appears to be larger than South America when, in reality, it is only one-eighth its size.

Direction

Any straight line drawn on this projection will represent an actual compass bearing. Such lines of true direction are referred to as *rhumb lines*, and generally do *not* describe the shortest distance between points.

Distance

The only true scale is along the Equator, or along the secant latitudes.

Limitations

The poles cannot be represented on the Mercator projection. All meridians can be projected but the upper and lower limits of latitude are approximately 80 degrees, north and south. Great area distortion makes the Mercator projection unsuitable for general geographic world maps.

Uses & applications

- Standard sea navigation charts (direction).

- Other directional uses:
  Air travel
  Wind direction
  Ocean currents

- Conformal world maps.

■ The best use of this projection's conformal properties applies to regions near the Equator, such as Indonesia and parts of the Pacific Ocean.

Projection definition

```
:PROJECTION MERCATOR
:UNITS _____
:PARAMETERS
Longitude of central meridian:
Latitude of true scale:
False easting (meters):
False northing (meters):
```

Subcommand usage

■ Units must be FEET, METERS, or units per meter.

■ Degrees must be entered as DD MM SS. Values of longitude west of the Prime Meridian and of latitude south of the Equator are negative.

■ The latitude of true scale is usually the Equator, but it doesn't have to be.

■ False easting and northing are real numbers and can be zero.

MILLER

Miller Cylindrical

This projection is similar to the Mercator projection except that the polar regions are not as areally distorted. This modification is accomplished by reducing the distance between lines of latitude as they approach the poles. The modification decreases the distortion in area but the compromise introduces distortion in local shape and direction.

Method of projection

Cylindrical projection. Meridians are parallel and equally spaced, the lines of latitude are parallel, and the distance between them increases toward the poles. Both poles are represented as straight lines.

Point of tangency

The Equator.

Linear graticules

All meridians and all parallels.

Properties

Shape

Minimally distorted between 45th parallels, increasingly toward the poles. Land masses are stretched more east to west than they are north to south.

Area

Distortion increases from the Equator toward the poles.

Direction

Local angles are correct only along the Equator.

Distance

Correct distance is measured along the Equator.

Limitations

Useful only as a world map.

Uses & applications

■ General-purpose world maps.

Projection definition

```
:PROJECTION MILLER
:UNITS _____
:PARAMETERS
Radius of the sphere of reference:
Longitude of central meridian:
False easting (meters):
False northing (meters):
```

Subcommand usage

■ Units must be FEET, METERS, or units per meter.

■ The radius of the sphere of reference is a real number. A zero can be entered to indicate the default radius: 6,370,997 meters.

■ This projection is supported only on a sphere. For information on using this projection with a datum or spheroid, refer to 'Projections on a sphere' in Appendix B of this book.

■ Degrees must be entered as DD MM SS. Values of longitude west of the Prime Meridian and of latitude south of the Equator are negative.

■ False easting and northing are real numbers and can be zero.

MOLLWEIDE

Mollweide, Babinet, Elliptical, Homolographic, and Homalographic

This pseudocylindrical projection was created by Carl B. Mollweide in 1805. It is an equal-area projection designed for small-scale maps.

Method of projection

A pseudocylindrical equal-area projection, on which all parallels are straight lines and all meridians are equally spaced elliptical arcs, except the central meridian, which is a straight line. The poles are points.

Linear graticules

The Equator and central meridian.

Properties

Shape

Shape is not distorted at the intersection of the central meridian and latitudes 40°44' N and S. Distortion increases outward from these points and becomes severe at the edges of the projection.

Area

Equal-area.

Direction

Local angles are true only at the intersection of the central meridian and latitudes 40°44' N and S. Direction is distorted elsewhere.

Distance

Scale is true along latitudes 40°44' N and S. Distortion increases with distance from these lines and becomes severe at the edges of the projection.

Limitations

Useful only as a world map.

Uses & applications

■ Suitable for thematic or distribution mapping of the entire world, frequently in interrupted form.

■ Combined with the Sinusoidal to create Goode's Homolosine and Boggs.

Projection definition

```
:PROJECTION MOLLWEIDE
:UNITS _____
:PARAMETERS
Longitude of projection center:
```

Subcommand usage

■ Units must be FEET, METERS, or units per meter.

■ Degrees must be entered as DD MM SS. Values west of the Prime Meridian are negative.

■ This projection is supported only on a sphere. For information on using this projection with a datum or spheroid, refer to 'Projections on a sphere' in Appendix B of this book.

NEWZEALAND_GRID

New Zealand National Grid

This is the standard projection for large-scale maps of New Zealand.

Method of projection

Modified cylindrical. A sixth-order conformal modification of a Mercator using the International spheroid.

Points of tangency

41° 00' S, 173° 00' E

Linear graticules

None.

Properties

Shape

Conformal. Local shapes are correct.

Area

Minimal distortion, less than 0.04 percent for New Zealand.

Direction

Minimal distortion within New Zealand.

Distance

Scale is within 0.02 percent of true scale for New Zealand.

Limitations

Not useful for areas outside New Zealand.

Uses & applications

■ New Zealand.

Projection definition

```
:PROJECTION NEWZEALAND_GRID
:UNITS _____
:PARAMETERS
```

Projection-specific parameters are set by the software.

Subcommand usage

■ Units must be FEET, METERS, or units per meter. For the units to be equivalent to decimal yards, enter 0.91408, since there are 1.0939 yards in a meter.

OBLIQUE_MERCATOR

Oblique Mercator, Oblique Cylindrical Orthomorphic, Hotine

This is an oblique rotation of the Mercator projection. Developed for conformal mapping of areas that do not follow a north-south or east-west trend but are obliquely oriented.

Method of projection

Cylindrical. Oblique aspect of the Mercator projection.

Line of tangency

A single oblique great-circle line. Or instead, there can be secancy along two oblique small circles parallel to and equidistant from the central great circle.

Linear graticules

Two meridians 180° apart.

Properties

Shape

Conformal. Local shapes are true.

Area

Distortion increases with distance from the central line.

Direction

Local angles are correct.

Distance

True along the chosen central line.

Limitations

Use should be limited to regions near the central line. When using an ellipsoid, constant scale along the central line and perfect conformality cannot be maintained simultaneously.

Uses & applications

■ Ideal for conformal mapping of regions trending in an oblique direction.

■ Large-scale mapping in Switzerland, Borneo, and Madagascar.

■ Alaskan panhandle.

Projection definition

```
:PROJECTION OBLIQUE_MERCATOR
:UNITS _____
:PARAMETERS
Enter projection type <1 | 2>:
```

Type 1

```
Scale factor at the projection's center:
Latitude of the projection's center:
Longitude of 1st point on the central line:
Latitude of 1st point on the central line:
Longitude of 2nd point on the central line:
Latitude of 2nd point on the central line:
False easting (meters):
False northing (meters):
```

Type 2

```
Scale factor at the projection's center:
Longitude of the projection's center:
Latitude of the projection's center:
Azimuth at the projection's center:
False easting (meters):
False northing (meters):
```

Subcommand usage

■ Units must be FEET, METERS, or units per meter.

■ Type 1 uses a central line defined by two points.

■ Type 2 uses a central line defined by one point and its angle of azimuth.

■ The scale factor is a real number, usually one.

■ Degrees must be entered as DD MM SS. Values of longitude west of the Prime Meridian and of latitude south of the Equator are negative.

■ Azimuth must be entered as an angle in decimal degrees.

■ False easting and northing are real numbers and can be zero.

■ May also be specified by OBLIQUE or HOTINE.

ORTHOGRAPHIC

Orthographic

The perspective of the projection views the globe from an infinite distance. This perspective gives the illusion of a three-dimensional globe. Distortion in size and area near the projection limit appear more realistic to our eye than that seen in almost any other projection, except the PERSPECTIVE.

Method of projection

Planar perspective projection, viewed from infinity. On the polar-aspect projection meridians are straight lines radiating from the center, and the lines of latitude are projected as concentric circles that become closer toward the edge of the globe. Only one hemisphere can be shown without overlapping.

Point of tangency

A single point located anywhere on the globe.

Linear graticules

All aspects - The central meridian of the projection.

Equatorial aspect - All lines of latitude.

Polar aspect - All meridians.

Properties

Shape

Minimal distortion near the center; maximal distortion near the edge.

Area

The areal scale decreases with distance from the center. Areal scale is zero at the edge of the hemisphere.

Direction

True direction from the central point.

Distance

The radial scale decreases with distance from the center and becomes zero on the edges. The scale perpendicular to the radii, along the parallels of the polar aspect, is accurate.

Limitations

Limited to a view 90 degrees from the central point, a global hemisphere.

Uses & applications

■ Uses of this projection are aesthetic more than technical. The most commonly used aspect for this purpose is the oblique.

Projection definition

```
:PROJECTION ORTHOGRAPHIC
:UNITS _____
:PARAMETERS
Radius of the sphere of reference:
Longitude of center of projection:
Latitude of center of projection:
False easting (meters):
False northing (meters):
```

Subcommand usage

■ Units must be FEET, METERS, or units per meter.

■ The radius of the sphere of reference is a real number. A zero can be entered to indicate the default radius: 6,370,997 meters.

■ This projection is supported only on a sphere. For information on using this projection with a datum or spheroid, refer to 'Projections on a sphere' in Appendix B of this book.

■ Degrees must be entered as DD MM SS. Values of longitude west of the Prime Meridian and of latitude south of the Equator are negative.

■ False easting and northing are real numbers and can be zero.

PERSPECTIVE

Vertical Near-Side Perspective, Vertical Perspective

This projection is similar to the ORTHOGRAPHIC in that its perspective is from space. In this projection, the perspective point is not an infinite distance away; instead, the distance can be specified by the user. The overall effect of this projection is that it looks like a photograph taken vertically from a satellite or space vehicle.

Method of projection

Planar perspective projection. The distance above the Earth is variable and must be specified before the projection can be calculated. The greater the distance, the more closely this projection resembles the ORTHOGRAPHIC projection. All aspects are circular projections of an area less than a hemisphere.

Point of tangency

A single point anywhere on the globe.

Linear graticules

All aspects - The central meridian of the projection.

Polar aspect - All meridians.

Equatorial aspect - The Equator.

Properties

Shape

Minimally distorted near the center, increasing toward the edge.

Area

Minimally distorted near the center; the area scale then decreases to zero on the edge or horizon.

Direction

True directions from the point of tangency.

Distance

Radial scale decreases from true scale at the center to zero on the projection edge. The scale perpendicular to the radii decreases, but not as rapidly.

Limitations

The actual range depends on the distance from the globe. In all cases, the range is less than 90 degrees from the center.

Uses & applications

■ Used as an aesthetic presentation, rather than for technical applications.

Projection definition

```
:PROJECTION PERSPECTIVE
:UNITS _____
:PARAMETERS
Radius of the sphere of reference:
Height of perspective point above sphere:
Longitude of center of projection:
Latitude of center of projection:
False easting (meters):
False northing (meters):
```

Subcommand usage

■ Units must be FEET, METERS, or units per meter.

■ The radius of the sphere of reference is a real number. A zero can be entered to indicate the default radius: 6,370,997 meters.

■ This projection is supported only on a sphere. For information on using this projection with a datum or spheroid, refer to 'Projections on a sphere' in Appendix B of this book.

■ Height of the perspective point is entered in meters.

■ Degrees must be entered as DD MM SS. Values of longitude west of the Prime Meridian and of latitude south of the Equator are negative.

■ False easting and northing are real numbers, and can be zero.

POLAR

Universal Polar Stereographic, UPS, or Polar Stereographic

The Polar Stereographic may be used to accommodate all regions not included in the UTM Coordinate System, regions north of 84° N and 80° S. The projection is equivalent to the polar aspect of the Stereographic projection on a spheroid. The central point is either the North Pole or the South Pole. This is the only polar aspect planar projection that is conformal.

Method of projection

Planar perspective projection, where one pole is viewed from the other pole. Lines of latitude are concentric circles. The distance between circles increases with distance from the central pole.

Point of tangency

A single point, either the North Pole or the South Pole. If the plane is secant instead of tangent, the point of global contact is a line of latitude.

Linear graticules

All meridians.

Properties

Shape

Conformal; accurate representation of local shapes.

Area

The farther from the pole, the greater the areal scale.

Direction

True direction from the pole. Local angles are true everywhere.

Distance

The scale increases with distance from the center. If a standard parallel is chosen rather than one of the poles, this latitude represents the true scale, and the scale nearer the pole is reduced.

Limitations

Normally not extended more than 90° from the central pole, because of increased scale and area distortion.

Uses & applications

■ Polar regions (conformal).

■ In the UPS system, the scale factor at the pole is made 0.994, thus making the standard parallel (latitude of true scale) approximately 81° 07' N or S.

Projection definition

```
:PROJECTION POLAR
:UNITS _____
:PARAMETERS
Longitude of central meridian:
Latitude of true scale:
False easting (meters):
False northing (meters):
```

Subcommand usage

■ Units must be FEET, METERS, or units per meter.

■ Ellipsoid projections of the polar regions require the additional command, normally SPHEROID INT1909, before the parameters are specified.

■ Degrees must be entered as DD MM SS. Values of longitude west of the Prime Meridian and of latitude south of the Equator are negative.

■ The latitude of true scale is used to differentiate tangential projections from secant projections.

■ For tangential projections, specify the latitude of true scale as the North Pole, 90 00 00, or the South Pole, -90 00 00.

■ For secant projections, specify the latitude of true scale as any line of latitude other than 90° N or S.

■ False easting and northing are real numbers and can be zero.

■ Use the UPS projection for projecting to or from the Universal Polar Stereographic system.

POLYCONIC

Polyconic

The name of this projection translates into 'many cones' and refers to the projection methodology. This affects the shape of the meridians. Unlike other conic projections, the meridians are curved, rather than linear.

Method of projection

More complex than the regular conic projections, but still a simple construction. This projection is created by lining up an infinite number of cones along the central meridian. This projection yields parallels that are *not* concentric. Each line of latitude represents the base of its tangential cone.

Lines of tangency

MANY lines; all parallels of latitude in the projection.

Linear graticules

Central meridian of the projection, and the Equator.

Properties

Shape

No local shape distortion along the central meridian. Distortion increases with distance from the central meridian, thus distortion to the east and west is greater than distortion to the north and south.

Area

Distortion in area increases with distance from the central meridian.

Direction

Local angles are accurate along the central meridian; otherwise, distorted.

Distance

The scale along each parallel and along the central meridian of the projection is accurate. It increases along the meridians as the distance from the central meridian increases.

Limitations

Distortion is minimized on large-scale maps, such as topographic quadrangles, where meridians and parallels can be drawn in practice as straight-line segments. Producing a map library with this kind of map sheet is not advised because errors accumulate and become visible when joining sheets in multiple directions.

Uses & applications

■ 7 1/2- and 15-minute topographic USGS quad sheets, from 1886 until approximately 1957. Note: Some new quad sheets after this date have been falsely documented as Polyconic. The present projection for east-west State Plane Coordinate System zones is LAMBERT, and TRANSVERSE for north-south state zones.

Projection definition

```
:PROJECTION POLYCONIC
:UNITS METERS
:PARAMETERS
Longitude of central meridian:
Latitude of projections origin:
False easting (meters):
False northing (meters):
```

Subcommand usage

■ Units must be FEET, METERS, or units per meter.

■ Degrees must be entered as DD MM SS. Values of longitude west of the Prime Meridian and of latitude south of the Equator are negative.

■ False easting and northing are real numbers and can be zero.

ROBINSON

Robinson or Orthophanic

Method of projection

Pseudocylindrical. Meridians are equally spaced and resemble elliptical arcs, concave toward the central meridian. The central meridian is a straight line 0.51 times the length of the Equator. Parallels are equally spaced straight lines between 38° N and S; spacing decreases beyond these limits. The poles are 0.53 times the length of the Equator. The projection is based upon tabular coordinates instead of mathematical formulas.

Linear graticules

All parallels and the central meridian.

Properties

Shape

Shape distortion is very low within 45° of the origin and along the Equator.

Area

Distortion is very low within 45° of the origin and along the Equator.

Direction

Generally distorted.

Distance

Generally, scale is made true along latitudes 38° N and S. Scale is constant along any given latitude, and for the latitude of opposite sign.

Limitations

Neither conformal nor equal area. Useful only for world maps.

Uses & applications

■ Developed for use in general and thematic world maps.

■ Used by Rand McNally since the 1960s and by the National Geographic Society since 1988 for general and thematic world maps.

Projection definition

```
:PROJECTION ROBINSON
:UNITS _____
:PARAMETERS
Longitude of central meridian:
False easting (meters):
False northing (meters):
```

Subcommand usage

■ Units must be FEET, METERS, or units per meter.

■ Degrees must be entered as DD MM SS. Values of longitude west of the Prime Meridian and of latitude south of the Equator are negative.

■ False easting and northing are real numbers and can be zero.

RSO

Rectified Skewed Orthomorphic

This projection is provided with two options—for the national coordinate systems of Malaysia and Brunei—and is similar to the Oblique Mercator.

Method of projection

Oblique cylindrical projection. A line of true scale is drawn at an angle to the central meridian.

Point of tangency

A single, oblique, great-circle line.

Linear graticules

Two meridians 180 degrees apart.

Properties

Shape

Conformal. Local shapes are true.

Area

Distortion increases with distance from the central line.

Direction

Local angles are correct.

Distance

True along the chosen central line.

Limitations

Use should be limited to those areas of Brunei and Malaysia for which the projection was developed.

Uses & applications

■ Used as the national projections of Malaysia and Brunei.

Projection definition

```
:PROJECTION RSO
:UNITS _____
:PARAMETERS
Enter: Brunei (1) or Malaysia (2):
```

Subcommand usage

■ Units must be FEET, METERS, or units per meter.

■ Enter a 1 for projecting data within Brunei and 2 for data within Malaysia.

SIMPLE_CONIC

Simple Conic, Equidistant Conic, or Conic

This conic projection can be based on one or two standard parallels. As the name implies, all circular parallels are an equal distance from each other, spaced evenly along the meridians. This is true whether one or two parallels are used as the standards.

Method of projection

Cone is tangential if only one standard parallel is specified and secant for two standard parallels. Graticules are evenly spaced. The space between each meridian is equal, as is the space between each of the concentric arcs that describe the lines of latitude. The poles are represented as arcs rather than points.

Lines of contact

Depends on the number of standard parallels.

Tangential projections (Type 1) - One line, indicated by the standard parallel.

Secant projections (Type 2) - Two lines, specified as 1st and 2nd standard parallels.

Linear graticules

All meridians.

Properties

Shape

Local shapes are true along the standard parallels. Distortion is constant along any given parallel. Distortion increases with distance from the standard parallels.

Area

Distortion is constant along any given parallel. Distortion increases with distance from the standard parallels.

Direction

Locally true along the standard parallels.

Distance

True along the meridians and the standard parallels. Scale is constant along any given parallel, but changes from parallel to parallel.

Limitations

Range in latitude should be limited to 30 degrees.

Uses & applications

■ Regional mapping of mid-latitude areas with a predominantly east-west expanse.

■ Common for atlas maps of small countries.

■ Used by the Soviet Union for mapping the entire country.

Projection definition

```
:PROJECTION SIMPLE_CONIC
:UNITS _____
:PARAMETERS
Number of standard parallels < 1 | 2 >:
```

Type 1

```
Longitude of the central meridian (DMS):
Latitude of the origin (DMS):
Latitude of the standard parallel (DMS):
```

Type 2

```
Longitude of the central meridian (DMS):
Latitude of the origin (DMS):
Latitude of the 1st standard parallel (DMS):
Latitude of the 2nd standard parallel (DMS):
```

Subcommand usage

■ Units must be FEET, METERS, or units per meter.

■ Degrees must be entered as DD MM SS. Values of longitude west of the Prime Meridian and of latitude south of the Equator are negative.

■ If the pole is given as the single standard parallel, the cone becomes a plane and the resulting projection is the same as a polar Azimuthal Equidistant.

■ If two standard parallels are placed symmetrically north and south of the Equator, the resulting projection is the same as Equirectangular and the Equirectangular projection must be used.

■ If the standard parallel is the Equator, the Equirectangular projection must be used.

■ May also be specified by EQUIDISTANT.

SINUSOIDAL

Sinusoidal, Sanson-Flamsteed

As a world map, this projection maintains equal area despite conformal distortion. Alternative formats reduce the distortion along outer meridians by interrupting the continuity of the projection over the oceans and by recentering the continents around their own central meridians, or vice versa.

Method of projection

A pseudocylindrical projection where all parallels are straight. Horizontal lines and all meridians, other than the straight central meridian, are sinusoidal curves.

Linear graticules

All lines of latitude and the central meridian.

Properties

Shape

Free of distortion along the central meridian and the Equator. Smaller regions using the interrupted format exhibit less distortion than the uninterrupted sinusoidal projection of the world.

Area

Areas are represented accurately.

Direction

Local angles are correct along the central meridian and the Equator, but distorted elsewhere.

Distance

The scale along all parallels and the central meridian of the projection is accurate.

Limitations

Distortion is reduced when used for a single land mass, rather than the entire globe. This is especially true for regions near the Equator.

Uses & applications

■ World maps illustrating area characteristics, especially if interrupted.

■ Continental maps of South America, Africa, and occasionally others, where each land mass has its own central meridian.

Projection definition

```
:PROJECTION SINUSOIDAL
:UNITS METERS
:PARAMETERS
Radius of the sphere of reference:
Longitude of central meridian:
False easting (meters):
False northing (meters):
```

Subcommand usage

■ Units must be FEET, METERS, or units per meter.

■ The radius of the sphere of reference is a real number. A zero can be entered to indicate the default radius: 6,370,997 meters.

■ This projection is supported only on a sphere. For information on using this projection with a datum or spheroid, refer to 'Projections on a sphere' in Appendix B of this book.

■ Degrees must be entered as DD MM SS. Values of longitude west of the Prime Meridian and of latitude south of the Equator are negative.

SPACE_OBLIQUE_MERCATOR

Space Oblique Mercator

This projection is nearly conformal and has little scale distortion within the sensing range of an orbiting mapping satellite such as Landsat. This is the first projection to incorporate the Earth's rotation with respect to the orbiting satellite.

Method of projection

Modified cylindrical, for which the central line is curved and defined by the ground track of the orbit of the satellite.

Line of tangency

Conceptual.

Linear graticules

None.

Properties

Shape

Shape is correct within a few parts per million for the sensing range of the satellite.

Area

Varies by less than 0.02 percent for the sensing range of the satellite.

Direction

Minimal distortion within the sensing range.

Distance

Scale is true along the ground track, and varies approximately 0.01 percent within the sensing range.

Limitations

Plots for adjacent paths do not match without transformation.

Uses & applications

■ Specifically designed to minimize distortion within the sensing range of a mapping satellite as it orbits the rotating Earth.

■ Used for georectification of, and continuous mapping from, satellite imagery.

■ Standard format for data from Landsat 4 and 5.

Projection definition

```
:PROJECTION SPACE_OBLIQUE_MERCATOR
:UNITS _____
:PARAMETERS
Landsat vehicle ID (1,2,3,4,5):
Orbital path number (1-233):
```

Subcommand usage

■ Units must be FEET, METERS, or units per meter.

■ For Landsat 1, 2 and 3, the path range is from 1 to 251. For Landsat 4 and 5, the path range is from 1 to 233.

STATEPLANE

State Plane Coordinate System, SPCS

The State Plane Coordinate System is not a projection. It is a coordinate system that divides all fifty of the United States, Puerto Rico and the U.S. Virgin Islands into over 120 numbered sections, referred to as zones. Depending on its size, each state is represented by anywhere from one to ten zones. The shape of the zone then determines which projection is most suitable. Three projections are used: the Lambert Conic Conformal (LAMBERT) for zones running east and west, the Transverse Mercator (TRANSVERSE) for zones running north and south, and the Oblique Mercator (OBLIQUE_MERCATOR) for one zone only, the panhandle of Alaska. Each zone has an assigned code number, each having a designated central origin which is specified in degrees.

Method of projection

Projection may be cylindrical or conic. See LAMBERT, TRANSVERSE, and OBLIQUE_MERCATOR for methodology and properties.

Uses & applications

■ Standard USGS 7 1/2- and 15-minute quad sheets.

■ Used for most federal, state, and local large-scale mapping projects in the United States.

Projection definition

```
:PROJECTION STATEPLANE
:UNITS _____
:ZONE ____
:PARAMETERS
```

Subcommand usage

■ Units must be FEET, or METERS, or units per meter.

■ ZONE requires the USGS code number that refers to the region of the base map. These are selected values that range from 3101 to 6401. (Refer to *ARC Command References*.)

■ Projection-specific parameters are set by the software.

■ May also be specified as STATE.

Discussion

What is State Plane

The State Plane Coordinate System (SPCS) is a coordinate system designed for mapping the United States. It was developed in the 1930s by the U.S. Coast and Geodetic Survey to provide a common reference system to surveyors and mappers. The goal was to design a conformal mapping system for the country with a maximum scale distortion of 1 part in 10,000, then considered the limit of surveying accuracy.

Three conformal projections were chosen: the Lambert Conformal Conic for states that are longer in the east-west direction, such as Tennessee and Kentucky, the Transverse Mercator projection for states that are longer in the north-south direction, such as Illinois and Vermont, and the Oblique Mercator projection for the panhandle of Alaska, because it is neither predominantly north nor south, but at an angle.

To maintain an accuracy of 1 part in 10,000, it was necessary to divide many states into zones. Each zone has its own central meridian or standard parallels to maintain the desired level of accuracy within the zones. The boundaries of these zones follow county boundaries. Smaller states such as Connecticut required only one zone, whereas Alaska is composed of ten zones and uses all three projections.

This coordinate system is referred to here as the State Plane Coordinate System of 1927 (SPCS 27). It is based upon a network of geodetic control points referred to as the North American Datum of 1927 (NAD27).

Why use State Plane

The State Plane Coordinate System is used primarily by governmental organizations or groups who do work with them. Most often, these are county or municipal databases. The advantage of using SPCS is that your data will be in a common coordinate system which is the same as that of other databases covering the same area.

State Plane and the North American Datum

Technological advancements of the last fifty years have led to improvements in the measurement of distances, angles, and the Earth's size and shape. This, combined with moving the origin of the datum from Meades Ranch in Kansas to the Earth's center of mass, for compatibility with satellite systems, made it necessary to redefine SPCS 27. Consequently, the coordinates for points are different for SPCS 27 and SPCS 83. There are several reasons for this. For SPCS 83, all State Plane coordinates published by NGS are in metric units, the shape of the spheroid of the Earth is slightly different, some states have changed the definition of their zones, and values of latitude and longitude are slightly changed.

The following zone changes have been made from SPCS 27 to SPCS 83. In addition, false easting and northing, or origin, of most zones has changed.

■ California - California zone 7, SPCS 27 zone 0407, was eliminated and included in California zone 5 SPCS 83 zone 0405.

■ Montana - The three zones for Montana, SPCS 27 zones 2501, 2502, and 2503, were eliminated and replaced by a single zone, SPCS 83 zone 2500.

■ Nebraska - The two zones for Nebraska, SPCS 27 zones 2601 and 2602, were eliminated and replaced by a single zone, SPCS 83 zone 2600.

■ South Carolina - The two zones for South Carolina, SPCS 27 zones 3901 and 3902, were eliminated and replaced by a single zone, SPCS 83 zone 3900.

■ Puerto Rico and Virgin Islands - The two zones for Puerto Rico and the Virgin Islands, St. Thomas, St. John, and St. Croix, SPCS 27 zones 5201 and 5202, were eliminated and replaced by a single zone, SPCS 83 zone 5200.

Unit of length

The standard unit of length measurement for SPCS 27 is the U.S. Survey foot. For SPCS 83, the most common unit of measure is the meter. Those states that support both feet and meters have legislated which feet-to-meters conversion they use. The difference between the two is only two parts in one million, but that can become noticeable when data sets are stored in double precision.

■ The U.S. Survey foot equals 1200/3937 m, or 0.3048006096 m. This is the conversion used by ARC/INFO.

■ The international foot equals 0.3048 m exactly. To use the international foot when projecting data, specify 'UNITS 3.28084', since the international foot is 3.28084 units per meter.

Required use of DATUM

The State Plane Coordinate System exists on only two horizontal datums: NAD27 and NAD83. Therefore, to prevent misuse and ensure meta data is appropriately maintained, the DATUM option is required when the projection is specified as STATEPLANE. The only valid keywords for DATUM are NAD27, NAD83, and HPGN.

If DATUM is specified, it will default to NAD27.

If HPGN is specified as the DATUM, the NAD83 SPCS projection parameters will be used.

If this DATUM requirement creates a compatibility issue in your application, you should review your implementation to ensure that you are not inadvertently misusing the State Plane Coordinate System. You can work around this requirement by using the appropriate map projection and parameters instead of the STATEPLANE option. Refer to the following section for examples of projections and parameters used with the State Plane Coordinate System.

Example of zone definitions

Although STATEPLANE is an option for the PROJECT command, it is not a map projection. It is a coordinate system composed of three possible projections. The parameters defining these projections are set by law or other adoption, and are used by the software when the optional subcommands ZONE or FIPSZONE are specified.

Here is an example of SPCS 83 parameters:

State	Alabama East	Alabama West	Tennessee
ZONE	3101	3102	5301
FIPSZONE	0101	0102	4100
Projection	Transverse	Transverse	Lambert
Standard Parallels			35°15' 36°25'
Central Meridian	85°50'	87°30'	86°00'
Scale Factor Reduction at Central Meridian	1:25000	1:15000	
Latitude of Origin	30°30'	30°00'	34°20'
Longitude of Origin	85°50'	87°30'	86°00'
False Easting	200000	600000	600000
False Northing	0	0	0

STEREOGRAPHIC

Stereographic

Of all the azimuthal projections, this is the only one that is conformal. Although all aspects are possible for the spherical Earth with this software, the polar aspect also exists as a separate projection that includes the spheroidal formulas (see POLAR).

Method of projection

Planar perspective projection, viewed from the point on the globe opposite the point of tangency. All meridians and parallels are shown as circular arcs or straight lines. Graticular intersections are 90 degrees. In the equatorial aspect, the parallels curve in opposite directions on either side of the Equator. In the oblique case, only the parallel opposite in sign to the central latitude is a straight line; other parallels are concave toward the poles on either side of the straight parallel.

Point of tangency

A single point, any point on the globe. Points represented by the North Pole and the South Pole should be processed using POLAR.

Linear graticules

Polar aspect - All meridians.

Equatorial aspect - The central meridian and the Equator.

Oblique aspect - Central meridian, and parallel of latitude with sign opposite that of the central latitude.

Properties

Shape

Conformal. Local shape is accurate.

Area

True scale at center. Distortion increases with distance from the center.

Direction

From the center, directions are accurate. Local angles are accurate everywhere.

Distance

Scale increases with distance from the center.

Limitations

Normally limited to one hemisphere, a radius of 90 degrees from the center. Portions of the outer hemisphere may be shown, but with rapidly increasing distortion.

Uses & applications

■   The oblique aspect has been used to map circular regions on the Moon, Mars and Mercury.

Projection definition

```
:PROJECTION STEREOGRAPHIC
:UNITS _____
:PARAMETERS
Enter projection type <1 | 2>:
```

Type 1 parameters

```
Radius of the sphere of reference:
Longitude of center of projection:
Latitude of center of projection:
False easting (meters):
False northing (meters):
```

Type 2 parameters

```
Longitude of central meridian:
Latitude of projection's center:
View < EQUATORIAL | NORTHPOLE | SOUTHPOLE >:
Scale factor:                    (equatorial view)
or
Latitude of standard parallel:  (polar view)
```

Subcommand usage

■ Units must be FEET, METERS, or units per meter.

■ The radius of the sphere of reference is a real number. A zero can be entered to indicate the default radius: 6,370,997 meters.

■ This projection is supported only on a sphere. For information on using this projection with a datum or spheroid, refer to 'Projections on a sphere' in Appendix B of this book.

■ Degrees must be entered as DD MM SS. Values of longitude west of the Prime Meridian and of latitude south of the Equator are negative.

■ View must be answered with a keyword (EQUATORIAL, NORTHPOLE, or SOUTHPOLE).

■ False easting and northing are real numbers and can be zero.

TIMES

Bartholomew Times

The Times was developed by Moir in 1965 for Bartholomew. It is a modified Gall's Stereographic. Unlike Gall's, the Times has curved meridians.

Method of projection

Pseudocylindrical. Meridians are equally spaced curves. Parallels are straight lines increasing in separation with distance from the Equator.

Lines of secancy

Two lines at 45° N and S.

Linear graticules

All parallels and the central meridian.

Properties

Shape

Moderate distortion.

Area

Increasing distortion with distance from 45° N and S.

Direction

Generally distorted.

Distance

Scale is correct along parallels at 45° N and S.

Limitations

Useful only for world maps.

Uses & applications

- Used by Bartholomew in *The Times Atlas* for world maps.

Projection definition

```
:PROJECTION TIMES
:UNITS _____
:PARAMETERS
Radius of sphere of reference:
Longitude of projection center:
False easting:
False northing:
```

Subcommand usage

- Units must be FEET, METERS, or units per meter.

- The radius of the sphere of reference is a real number. A zero can be entered to indicate the default radius: 6,370,997 meters.

- This projection is supported only on a sphere. For information on using this projection with a datum or spheroid, refer to 'Projections on a sphere' in Appendix B of this book.

- Degrees must be entered as DD MM SS. Values of longitude west of the Prime Meridian and of latitude south of the Equator are negative.

- False easting and northing are real numbers and can be zero.

TRANSVERSE

Transverse Mercator

This projection is similar to the Mercator except that the cylinder is longitudinal along a meridian instead of the Equator. The result is a conformal projection that does not maintain true directions. The central meridian is centered on the region to be highlighted. This centering on a specific region minimizes distortion of all properties in that region. As meridians run north and south, this projection is best suited for land masses that also stretch north to south. The State Plane Coordinate System uses this projection for all state zones oriented north to south.

Method of projection

Cylindrical projection with central meridian centered along a particular region.

Lines of contact

Any single meridian for the tangent projection. For the secant projection, two parallel lines equidistant from the central meridian.

Linear graticules

The Equator and the central meridian.

Properties

Shape

Conformal. Small shapes are maintained. Shapes of larger regions are increasingly distorted away from the central meridian.

Area

Distortion increases with distance from the central meridian.

Direction

Local angles are accurate everywhere.

Distance

Accurate scale along the central meridian if its scale factor is specified as 1.0. If the scale factor of the central meridian is less than 1.0, then there are two straight lines having an accurate scale, equidistant from and on each side of the central meridian. See the 'Subcommand usage' note regarding the scale factor.

Limitations

Global projection becomes infinite 90 degrees from the central meridian. Use should be limited to 15 to 20 degrees on both sides of the central meridian.

Uses & applications

■ State Plane Coordinate System (SPCS), used for predominantly north-south state zones.

■ USGS 7 1/2-minute quad sheets to match the State Plane Coordinate System. This projection was used for most new maps after 1957. It replaced the previous Polyconic projection.

■ North America (USGS, central meridian scale factor = 0.926).

■ Topographic Maps of the Ordnance Survey of Great Britain, after 1920.

Projection definition

```
:PROJECTION TRANSVERSE
:UNITS _____
:PARAMETERS
Scale factor at central meridian:
Longitude of central meridian:
Latitude of origin:
False easting (meters):
False northing (meters):
```

Subcommand usage

■ Units must be FEET, METERS, or units per meter.

■ Degrees must be entered as DD MM SS. Values of longitude west of the Prime Meridian and of latitude south of the Equator are negative.

■ Scale factor is a real number, 1.0 or less. A scale factor less than 1.0 will result in a secant projection.

TWO_POINT_EQUIDISTANT

Two-point Equidistant

This projection shows true distance from either of two chosen points to any other point on a map.

Method of projection

Modified planar.

Points of tangency

None.

Linear graticules

Normally none.

Properties

Shape

Minimal distortion in the region of the two chosen points, if they're within 45 degrees of each other. Increasing distortion beyond this region.

Area

Minimal distortion in the region of the two chosen points, if they're within 45 degrees of each other. Increasing distortion beyond this region.

Direction

Varying distortion.

Distance

Correct from either of two chosen points to any other point on the map. Straight line from either point represents the correct great-circle length but not the correct great-circle path.

Limitations

Does not represent great-circle paths.

Uses & applications

■ Used by National Geographic Society for maps of Asia.

■ Adapted form used by Bell Telephone system for determining the distance used in calculating long distance telephone rates.

Projection definition

```
:PROJECTION TWO_POINT_EQUIDISTANT
:UNITS _____
:PARAMETERS
Longitude of point A:
Latitude of point A:
Longitude of point B:
Latitude of point B:
```

Subcommand usage

■ Units must be FEET, METERS, or units per meter.

■ Degrees must be entered as DD MM SS. Values of longitude west of the Prime Meridian and of latitude south of the Equator are negative.

■ Point A must be west of point B.

■ This projection is supported only on a sphere. For information on using this projection with a datum or spheroid, refer to 'Projections on a sphere' in Appendix B of this book.

UPS

Universal Polar Stereographic, UPS

This form of the Polar Stereographic accommodates all regions not included in the UTM Coordinate System, regions north of 84° N and 80° S. The projection is equivalent to the polar aspect of the Stereographic projection of the spheroid with specific parameters. The central point is either the North Pole or the South Pole. Of all the polar aspect planar projections, the Stereographic is the only conformal one.

Method of projection

Approximately (for the spheroid) planar perspective projection, where one pole is viewed from the other pole. Lines of latitude are concentric circles. The distance between circles increases away from the central pole. The origin at the intersection of meridians is assigned a false easting and false northing of 2,000,000 meters.

Lines of secancy

The parallel of approximately 81°07' N or S, provided by a scale factor of 0.994 at the pole.

Linear graticules

All meridians.

Properties

Shape

Conformal. Accurate representation of local shape.

Area

The farther from the pole, the greater the area scale.

Direction

True direction from the pole. Local angles are correct everywhere.

Distance

In general, the scale increases with distance from the pole. At latitude 81°07' N or S, true scale is maintained and the scale nearer the pole is reduced.

Limitations

The UPS is normally limited to 84° N in the north polar aspect and 80° S in the south polar aspect.

Uses & applications

- Conformal mapping of polar regions.

- Used for polar regions of UTM Coordinate System.

Projection definition

```
:PROJECTION UPS
:UNITS _____
:PARAMETERS
Pole < NORTHPOLE | SOUTHPOLE >:
```

Subcommand usage

■ Units must be entered as FEET, METERS, or units per meter.

■ The hemisphere must be entered using the keyword NORTHPOLE or SOUTHPOLE.

■ May also be specified by UNIVERSAL_POLAR_STEREOGRAPHIC.

UTM

Universal Transverse Mercator, UTM

For the Universal Transverse Mercator System, the globe is divided into sixty zones, each spanning six degrees of longitude. Each zone has its own central meridian. This projection is a specialized application of the Transverse Mercator projection. The limits of each zone are 84° N, 80° S. Regions beyond these limits are accommodated by the Universal Polar Stereographic projection (see POLAR or UPS).

Method of projection

Each UTM zone has its own central meridian from which it spans 3 degrees west and 3 degrees east of that central meridian. The cylindrical methodology is the same as that for the TRANSVERSE projection. Note that the position of the cylinder rotates systematically around the globe. x- and y-coordinates are recorded in meters. The origin for each zone is the Equator and its central meridian. To eliminate negative coordinates, the projection alters the coordinate values at the origin. The value given to the central meridian is the false easting, and the value assigned to the Equator is the false northing. A false easting of 500,000 is applied.

Lines of secancy

Two lines parallel to and approximately 180 km to each side of the central meridian of the UTM zone.

Linear graticules

The central meridian and the Equator.

Properties

Shape

Conformal. Accurate representation of small shapes. Minimal distortion of larger shapes within the zone.

Area

Minimal distortion within each UTM zone.

Direction

Local angles are true.

Distance

Scale is constant along the central meridian, but at a scale factor of 0.9996 to reduce lateral distortion within each zone. With this scale factor, lines lying 180 km east and west of and parallel to the central meridian have a scale factor of 1.

Limitations

Designed for a scale error not exceeding 0.1 percent within each zone. This projection spans the globe from 84° N to 80° S. Error and distortion increase for regions that span more than one UTM zone.

Uses & application

- United States topographic quadrangles, 1:100,000.

■ In the United States, the Clarke 1866 spheroid is most commonly used with UTM, except in Hawaii where the International 1909 is commonly used.

■ Large-scale topographic mapping of the Soviet Union.

■ Medium-scale maps of regions throughout the world.

Projection definition

Zone NOT specified...	*UTM zone specified...*
`:PROJECTION UTM`	`:PROJECTION UTM`
`:UNITS _____`	`:UNITS _____`
`:PARAMETERS`	`:ZONE _____`
`Longitude:`	`:PARAMETERS`
`Latitude:`	

Subcommand usage

■ Units must be entered as FEET, METERS, or units per meter.

■ An optional command is required to specify the UTM zone before the parameters are specified. Values range from 0 to 60. (Refer to *ARC Command References* for zone numbers.)

■ If the ZONE is specified, there are no parameter specifications to be answered.

■ If the ZONE is not identified before the parameters are specified, you will be prompted to specify any longitude and latitude value that exists in the coverage to be projected. Degrees must be entered as DD MM SS. Values of longitude west of the Prime Meridian and of latitude south of the Equator are negative. This will enable an internal calculation of the correct UTM zone.

■ A false northing for the southern hemisphere can be set using the YSHIFT optional subcommand. This value is usually 10,000,000 meters.

Datums and datum conversion

A datum is a set of parameters defining a coordinate system, and a set of control points whose geometric relationships are known, either through measurement or calculation (Dewhurst 1990). All datums are based upon a spheroid, which approximates the shape of the Earth.

There are many spheroids representing the shape of the Earth, and many more datums based upon them. One may more closely represent the shape of the surface of the Earth in a particular region. For a thorough discussion of spheroids, refer to the section titled 'The shape of the Earth' in Chapter 2 of this book.

A horizontal datum provides a frame of reference for measuring locations on the surface of the Earth. It defines the origin and orientation of lines of latitude and longitude. Because the Earth is a spheroid, not a perfect sphere, a local datum is limited in accuracy to a finite area surrounding its point of origin. An Earth-centered, or geocentric, datum, which relates coordinates on the Earth's surface to the Earth's center of mass, is potentially more accurate over a larger area.

In the last fifteen years, satellite data has provided geodesists with new measurements to define the best Earth-fitting ellipsoid, which relates coordinates to the Earth's center of mass. An Earth-centered datum does not have an initial point of origin like a local datum.

The Earth's center of mass is, in a sense, the origin. The most recently developed and widely used such datum is the World Geodetic System of 1984 (WGS84). It serves as the framework for supporting locational measurement worldwide. WGS84 is also the datum upon which GPS measurements are based.

Datum transformation

WGS84 provides a very convenient intermediate for transformation between datums and is available in ARC/INFO. There are two such transformations available. They are based upon the Molodensky and Bursa-Wolfe transformations, referred to as three- and seven-parameter transformations, respectively. These transformations use parameters published by the U.S. Defense Mapping Agency (DMA, 1991). Tables 6 through 14 of the PROJECT command reference contain lists of the name, keyword, spheroid, and applicable area for nearly 200 supported datums.

In addition to these methods, there are more specialized transformations available for North America, discussed later.

Three parameter (THREE)

The three-parameter transformation is similar to the traditional Molodensky transformation. This transformation accounts for shifts in the origin of the X, Y, and Z axes at the center of the Earth. This in essence is like sliding the latitude-longitude graticule across the surface of the Earth. The implementation used is slightly modified to improve the performance of the transformation near the poles.

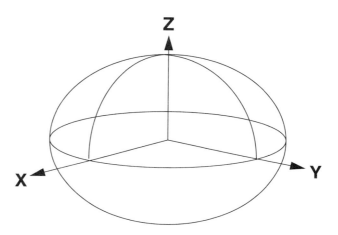

The following projection file would convert a data set from Scotland in the European datum of 1950 (ED50) to the Ordnance Survey of Great Britain datum of 1936, using the three-parameter transformation.

```
INPUT
PROJECTION GEOGRAPHIC
UNITS DD
DATUM EUR_K THREE
PARAMETERS
OUTPUT
PROJECTION GEOGRAPHIC
UNITS DD
DATUM OGB_C THREE
PARAMETERS
END
```

Seven parameter (SEVEN)

The seven-parameter transformation is also known as a Bursa-Wolfe transformation. This transformation accounts for the shifts in origin, as well as rotation about each of the three axes and a difference in scale.

The currently supported datums and keywords for the seven-parameter transformation are:

WGS72
WGS84

The values for these transformations were taken from (Soler and Hothem, 1989).

User-defined datums (USER_DEFINED)

In addition to supporting transformation between over two hundred known datums, there is a USER_DEFINED option to the DATUM subcommand. By supplying the correct shift parameters to get to or from WGS84, the intermediate datum, this option will allow you to transform between any two datums.

The parameters to be supplied are:

<dx, dy, dz> {rx, ry, rz, ds}

The first three required parameters, measured in meters, are the shifts of the origin; the other four optional parameters are rotation about each axis, measured in decimal seconds and the change in scale, measured in parts per million. When using the USER_DEFINED option, the spheroid should be specified using the SPHEROID subcommand or as the semi-major and semi-minor axis of the spheroid on the PARAMETERS line.

The following projection file would convert a WGS72 data set in Central America to an NAD83 data set.

```
INPUT
PROJECTION GEOGRAPHIC
UNITS DD
DATUM USER_DEFINED 0, 0, 4.5, 0, 0, -0.554, 0.227
SPHEROID WGS72
PARAMETERS
OUTPUT
PROJECTION GEOGRAPHIC
```

```
UNITS DD
DATUM NAR_D
PARAMETERS
END
```

Note: This could also have been done using

```
DATUM WGS72 SEVEN
```

instead of

```
DATUM USER_DEFINED 0, 0, 4.5, 0, 0, -0.554, 0.227
```

North American datums

There are two horizontal datums used almost exclusively in North America. These are the North American Datum of 1927 (NAD27) and the North American Datum of 1983 (NAD83).

NAD27

The North American Datum of 1927 uses the Clarke spheroid of 1866 to represent the shape of the Earth. The origin of this datum is a point on the Earth referred to as Meades Ranch in Kansas. Many NAD27 control points were calculated from observations taken in the 1800s. These calculations were done manually and in sections over many years. Therefore, errors varied from station to station.

NAD83

Many technological advances in surveying and geodesy since the establishment of NAD27—electronic theodolites, GPS satellites, Very Long Baseline Interferometry, and Doppler systems— revealed weaknesses in the existing network of control points. Differences became particularly noticeable when linking existing control with newly established surveys. The establishment of a new datum would allow for a single datum to cover North America and surrounding areas, consistently.

The North American Datum of 1983 is based upon both Earth and satellite observations, using the GRS80 spheroid. The origin for this datum is the Earth's center of mass. This affects the surface location of all latitude-longitude values enough to cause locations of previous control points in North America to shift, sometimes as much as 500 feet. A ten-year multinational effort tied together a network of control points for the United States, Canada, Mexico, Greenland, Central America, and the Caribbean.

Transforming between NAD27 and NAD83

Adoption of the North American Datum of 1983 requires that users store and use their map data in a coordinate system based upon NAD83. However, many of these users automated their original data layers using NAD27 and continue to do so, primarily because most source data is collected from maps based upon NAD27.

Due to differences in the method for defining each datum, as well as variations in distortion, the relationship between the NAD27 and NAD83 datum cannot be defined at every location by a single mathematical equation. A number of methods have been proposed for performing the datum adjustment. The currently accepted method is an error-averaging, rubber sheeting approach. A regular grid of control points whose datum shifts are known is used to estimate the shift at other locations.

Two such methods for transforming between NAD27 and NAD83 have been developed by the United States and Canada for use in their respective countries.

United States method (NADCON)

The datum transformation program known as NADCON, created by the U.S. National Geodetic Survey (NGS), has been implemented within the PROJECT command. The transformation of points has been determined from a minimum curvature-derived surface based upon the National Geodetic Reference System and has an approximate accuracy of 0.15 to 0.5 meters. The accepted national standard, this level of accuracy is the fastest, simplest, and most accurate datum transformation for mapping at scales of 1:200 and smaller. NADCON, an acronym for North American Datum CONversion, is suitable for the United States, Puerto Rico, and the Virgin Islands, but only for conversion between the NAD27, the NAD83, the High Precision GPS Network (HPGN) readjustment of NAD83, and selected local island datums discussed below.

To transform datum specify different input and output datums with the DATUM subcommand. The following projection file would convert an NAD27 data set to an NAD83 data set.

```
INPUT
PROJECTION STATEPLANE
UNITS FEET
ZONE 3426
DATUM NAD27 NADCON
PARAMETERS
OUTPUT
PROJECTION STATEPLANE
UNITS METERS
ZONE 3426
DATUM NAD83 NADCON
PARAMETERS
END
```

The following keywords (and associated regional coverage) are valid datum names when using the NADCON method for datum transformation.

Table 1:

Keyword	Region	Latitude	Longitude
NAD27	Coterminous United States	24 through 50	-66 through -126
	Alaska	50 through 74	-128 through 169
	Puerto Rico and the Virgin Islands	17 through 19	-64 through -68
OLD_HAWAIIAN	Hawaii	18 through 23	-154 through -161
ALASKAN_ISLAND	St. George	56 through 57	-169 through -171
	St. Lawrence	62 through 64	-168 through -172
	St. Paul	57 through 58	-169 through -171
NAD83	Encompasses all the above list areas		
HPGN	See list of supported states in the following section.		

The OLD_HAWAIIAN and ALASKAN_ISLAND keywords should be used to transform from the old island datum to NAD83. If your data is already in NAD27, do not use these options.

Accuracy and uncertainty

Following is a statement from the release notes of NADCON Version 2.1, October, 1993.

"The accuracy of the transformation should be viewed with some caution. At the 67 percent confidence level, this method introduces approximately 0.15 m uncertainty within the coterminous United States, 0.50 m uncertainty within Alaska, 0.20 m uncertainty within Hawaii, and 0.50 m uncertainty within Puerto Rico and the Virgin Islands. In areas of sparse geodetic data coverage NADCON may yield less accurate results, but seldom in excess of 1.0 m. Transformations between NAD83 and the States/Regions with High Accuracy Reference Networks (HARN) introduce approximately 0.05 m uncertainty. Transformations between old datums (NAD27, Old Hawaiian, Puerto Rico, etc.) and HARN could combine uncertainties (i.e., NAD27 to HARN equals 0.15m + 0.05m = 0.20m). In near offshore regions, results will be less accurate but seldom in excess of 5.0 m. Farther offshore, NAD27 was undefined. Therefore, the NADCON computed transformations are extrapolations and no accuracy can be stated."

State readjustments

There is an ongoing effort at the state level to readjust the NAD83 datum to a higher level of accuracy using state-of-the-art surveying techniques that were not widely available when the NAD83 datum was being developed. This project, known as the High Accuracy Reference Network (HARN), or High Precision GPS Network (HPGN) is a cooperative project between the National Geodetic Survey and the individual states.

To convert a data set in NAD27 or NAD83 to this newly readjusted network, use the DATUM option HPGN.

The following states are currently available in ARC/INFO:

Alabama
Colorado
Delaware
Florida
Idaho
Louisiana

Maryland
Montana
Oregon
Tennessee
Washington
Wisconsin

As other states are completed, they will be included in future releases of the software.

Why Y-coordinates may seem 200 meters too large

Nearly all published statements about the amount of shift between NAD27 and NAD83 are shifts measured in meters on unprojected (latitude-longitude) data. When two data sets are projected into planar coordinates (such as UTM or State Plane) and the differences between locations in NAD27 and NAD83 are measured, the Y-coordinate is often approximately 200 meters larger than expected. This is a result of the difference between the size and origin of the two spheroids upon which the data is being projected.

To prove this to yourself, you can create a coverage of a single arc, running along a meridian from the equator to your point of interest in the coterminous United States. By default, it will be created on the Clarke 1866 spheroid. Now PROJECT it and change the datum to NAD83. The arc should be approximately 200 meters longer.

Canadian method (CNT)

Canada's standard transformation program between NAD27 and NAD83 was developed by the Canadian Geodetic Survey. It is known within Canada as the National Transformation, and will be referred to in this document and the software as the Canadian National Transformation. The {method} keyword for use in the DATUM option of the PROJECT command is CNT. This transformation and its implementation are similar to the NADCON program used by the United States. The CNT method will only recognize NAD27 and NAD83 as datum name keywords.

This transformation predicts to within 0.01 m of the actual difference for 74% of the cases, and within 0.5 m for 93% of the cases.

ARC/INFO Version 7 uses Rev 1.0 of the Canadian National Transformation. Future releases will include updates to this program as they become available.

Rev 2.0, not in general release as of this printing, will include a higher-density grid spacing for the transformation in areas of particular interest. This will result in a more reliable transformation in major urban centers, or other areas that are densified.

The following projection file would convert an NAD27 data set to an NAD83 data set.

```
INPUT
PROJECTION UTM
UNITS METERS
DATUM NAD27 CNT
ZONE 15
PARAMETERS
OUTPUT
PROJECTION UTM
UNITS METERS
DATUM NAD83 CNT
ZONE 15
PARAMETERS
END
```

Using the three-parameter method in North America

There are two cases in which it may be necessary to use the three-parameter transformation for datum transformation in North America: when the data needs to be converted to or from a datum other than NAD27 or NAD83, or when the data falls in an area not covered by United States or Canadian solutions. In these cases, the results of the three-parameter transformation will result in errors or uncertainty up to 50 m, which is adequate for mapping at 1:65,000 or smaller.

You may also want to use the three-parameter transformation to change the datum of a three-arc second DEM that is in WGS72, to match a database stored in NAD83, or to transform from NAD27 to NAD83 in Mexico, Central America, Greenland, or the Caribbean.

The following projection file would convert a WGS72 data set to an NAD83 data set.

```
INPUT
PROJECTION GEOGRAPHIC
UNITS DS
DATUM WGS72 SEVEN
PARAMETERS
OUTPUT
PROJECTION UTM
UNITS METERS
DATUM NAR_D THREE
ZONE 17
PARAMETERS
END
```

Datum conversion using ADJUST

In cases where the required input or output datum cannot be converted using the standard methods listed above, you can build links between common points on data sets in both datums and perform an ADJUST. This could introduce a distortion of 1 to 5 meters or more into the transformed coordinate values (accuracy depends upon the accuracy of the original data and establishment of the links). This value is reasonable for most data sets—a recent survey by the National Geodetic Survey found that many map databases (including those which were digitized from map sources of varying quality) had absolute positional errors as large as 75 to 100 feet.

The ADJUST command can be used for datum conversion if errors on the order of more than 1 meter are acceptable. In these cases, use the process described here to perform the adjustment.

Step 1: Project the data set to be adjusted into geographic (latitude-longitude) coordinates

The adjustment must take place in coordinates of decimal degrees. Here is a sample projection file for converting a coverage from the State Plane coordinate system:

```
INPUT
PROJECTION STATEPLANE
ZONE 3426
UNITS FEET
PARAMETERS
OUTPUT
PROJECTION GEOGRAPHIC
UNITS DD
PARAMETERS
END
```

Step 2: Establish a set of links to be used for the datum adjustment

Each link has a control point for its from-location and ends at a control point (i.e., its new location). These links provide the from- and to-points for the coverage adjustment.

Enough links should be used so that the extent of the entire coverage to be converted is enclosed in a convex hull created by connecting the outermost links. Feature coordinates outside the convex hull will not be adjusted, so use links from surrounding areas for the adjustment. When adjusting smaller-scale coverages (such as those based upon 1:63,360 and 1:250,000 scale maps), use links at each 7 1/2-minute interval. This will help generate a more accurate adjustment of all features in the coverage.

If you know the coordinate locations of the from- and to-points, then type them in. Using the screen cursor to graphically select control points can be inaccurate.

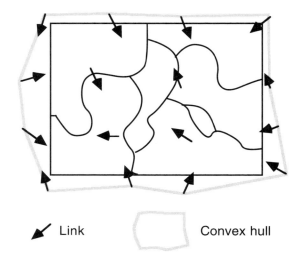

✎ Link   ⬡ Convex hull

Step 3: Perform the adjustment on the desired data set

This is done with the ADJUST command and the link coverage
generated in Step 2. ADJUST performs rubber sheeting using a link
coverage's from- and to-coordinates. The result is a coverage in
latitude-longitude coordinates based upon the new datum.

Before using ADJUST, you should decide whether or not to adjust
tics in the output coverage. You must explicitly tell ADJUST to
include tics in the adjustment; otherwise, the output coverage will
maintain the original tic locations. This is an important
consideration because your adjusted map will no longer overlay
(i.e., register to) the original source map, which was based upon the
input datum.

Step 4: Convert the adjusted data set into an appropriate map projection

The new projection for the coverage must be based upon the output
datum. For example, the following projection file can be used to
transform a coverage in latitude-longitude to State Plane
Coordinate System zone 3426:

```
INPUT
PROJECTION GEOGRAPHIC
UNITS DD
PARAMETERS
OUTPUT
PROJECTION STATEPLANE
ZONE 3426
DATUM NAD83
UNITS FEET
PARAMETERS
END
```

Projections on a sphere

Not all map projections use a spheroidal representation of the Earth. Some projections are only supported on a sphere. These projections are meant to be used at small scales, where the difference between a spherical and spheroidal representation of the Earth is smaller than the acceptable error of the map.

You should not try to project data from such a projection on a sphere to a projection on a spheroid and datum. The mathematical transformation does not exist. It is not possible to improve the geodetic precision of data by simply putting it onto a spheroidal representation of the Earth.

However, it is possible to project data from a projection on a datum to a projection on a sphere. This will degrade the data by putting it onto a spherical representation of the Earth, and can be done by the DATUM NONE option, and specifying the SPHEROID as SPHERE.

The following projection file would convert a UTM, NAD83 data set to Mollweide on a sphere.

```
INPUT
PROJECTION UTM
UNITS METERS
DATUM NAD83 NADCON
ZONE 12
```

```
PARAMETERS
OUTPUT
PROJECTION MOLLWEIDE
UNITS METERS
DATUM NONE
SPHEROID SPHERE
PARAMETERS
-110 00 00
END
```

The following projections are supported only on a sphere:

Azimuthal Equidistant
Bipolar Oblique Conic Conformal
Chamberlin Trimetric
Craster Parabolic
Cylindrical Equal-area
Eckert 4
Eckert 6
Equirectangular
Flat Polar Quartic
Gall Stereographic
Gnomonic
Grinten
Hammer-Aitoff
Lambert Azimuthal
Miller
Mollweide
Orthographic
Sinusoidal
Stereographic
Times
Vertical Near Side Perspective

Further considerations

Datum adjustment raises a number of important questions about how geographic data are maintained in ARC/INFO. For example:

"How are new map features automated to update ED50 coverages?", "What base map is to be used?", "If my base map is out of date (i.e., in NAD27 coordinates), what process do I use to add new features?", and so on. Consider each of these issues when refining your processing procedures to incorporate a new datum. More detailed information on datums can be found in the 'References' section at the end of this book.

Azimuthal Projection See Planar Projection.

Central Meridian The line of longitude which defines the x-coordinate origin of the projection.

Circle A geometric shape for which the distance from the center to any point on the edge is equal.

Conformal Projection Projection on which all angles at each point are preserved. Also called an orthomorphic projection (Snyder and Voxland, 1989).

Conic Projection Projection resulting from the conceptual projection of the Earth onto a tangent or secant cone, which is then cut lengthwise and laid flat (Snyder and Voxland, 1989).

Cylindrical Projection Projection resulting from the conceptual projection of the Earth onto a tangent or secant cylinder, which is then cut lengthwise and laid flat (Snyder and Voxland, 1989).

Datum A datum is a set of parameters defining a coordinate system, and a set of control points whose geometric relationships are known, either through measurement or calculation (Dewhurst, 1990).

Ellipse A geometric shape equivalent to a circle that is viewed obliquely.

Ellipsoid When used to represent the Earth, the three-dimensional shape obtained by rotating an ellipse about its minor axis. This is an ellipsoid of rotation, also called a spheroid.

Ellipticity The degree to which an ellipse deviates from a true circle. The degree of 'flattening' of an ellipse, measured as 1.0 minus the ratio of the minor axis to the major axis.

Equal-area (Equivalent) Projection Projection on which the areas of all regions are shown in the same proportion to their true areas. Shapes may be greatly distorted (Snyder and Voxland, 1989).

Equator The parallel of reference, 0° north or south.

Equidistant Projection Projection which maintains the scale along one or more lines, or from one or two points to all other points on the map.

Graticule Network of lines representing a selection of the Earth's parallels and meridians. (Snyder and Voxland, 1989).

Great Circle Any circle on the surface of a sphere formed by the intersection of the surface with a plane passing through the center of the sphere. It is the shortest path between any two points along the circle and therefore important to navigation. All meridians and the Equator are great circles on the Earth taken as a sphere (Snyder and Voxland, 1989).

Greenwich Prime Meridian The meridian of reference, 0° east or west.

Latitude The angular distance in degrees north or south of the equator. Lines of latitude are also referred to as *parallels*.

Longitude The angular distance in degrees east or west of the Greenwich Prime Meridian.

Major Axis The longer axis of an ellipse.

Map Projection A systematic conversion of locations on the world from spherical to planar coordinates.

Meridian Reference line on the Earth's surface formed by the intersection of the surface with a plane passing through both poles and some third point on the surface. This line is identified by its longitude (Snyder and Voxland, 1989).

Minor Axis The shorter axis of an ellipse.

Planar Projection Projection resulting from the conceptual projection of the Earth onto a tangent or secant plane. Usually, a planar projection is the same as an azimuthal projection (Snyder and Voxland, 1989).

Radius The distance from the outer edge of a circle to its center.

Reference Ellipsoid See Ellipsoid.

Rhumb Line Complex curve on the Earth's surface that crosses every meridian at the same oblique angle; a straight line on the Mercator projection. Also called a *loxodrome* (Snyder and Voxland, 1989).

Scale Factor Ratio of the scale at a particular location and direction on a map to the stated scale of the map (Snyder and Voxland, 1989).

Sphere The three-dimensional shape obtained by rotating a circle about an axis defined by its diameter.

Spherical Coordinate System A system using positions of latitude and longitude to define the locations of points on the surface of a sphere or spheroid.

Spheroid An ellipsoid that approximates a sphere. See Ellipsoid.

Standard Line A line having no distortion; commonly, a standard parallel or central meridian.

Standard Parallel The line of latitude which defines the origin of the Y-coordinate origin for the projection.

True-direction Projection Projection which represents great circle arcs with correct azimuths from one or two points. Alternatively, a map of limited extent can show great circle arcs as straight lines, although the azimuths will be incorrect.

References

Dewhurst, Warren T., *The Application of Minimum-curvature-derived Surfaces in the Transformation of Positional Data from the North American Datum of 1927 to the North American Datum of 1983*. NOAA Technical Memorandum NOS NGS-50. Rockville, MD: NOAA. January 1990.

DMA TR 8350.2, *Department of Defense World Geodetic System 1984*, Second Edition, 1991.

Greenhood, David. *Mapping*. Chicago: University of Chicago Press. 1964. 289pp.

Hradilek, L. and A. C. Hamilton. *A Systematic Analysis of Distortions in Map Projections*. Dept. of Surveying Engineering. Fredericton, New Brunswick: U.N.B. 1973. 37pp.

Junkins, D.R. (1988), *Transforming to NAD83*, Papers for the CISM Seminars on the NAD83 Redefinition in Canada and the Impact on Users, Canadian Institute of Surveying and Mapping.

Lee, J.E., and J.M. Walsh. *Map Projections for use with the Geographic Information System*. U.S. Fish Wildlife Services. FWS/OBS-84/17. 1984. 60pp.

Maling, D.H. *Coordinate Systems and Map Projections*. London: George Philip & Son, Ltd. 1973. 255pp.

NADCON Release Notes, README file accompanying NADCON Version 2.1, October, 1993, NOAA/NGS.

The North American Datum of 1983, A Collection of Papers Describing the Planning and Implementation of the Readjustment of the North American Horizontal Network. American Association for Geodetic Surveying, Monograph No. 2. ACSM, Falls Church, VA. 49pp.

Pearson, Frederick II. *Map Projections: Theory and Applications*. Boca Raton, Florida: CRC Press. 1990.

Radcliffe, John. "Considerations of ARC-PROJECT, ARC-TRANSFORM, MAP-PROJECTIONS, MAP-SCALE, Digitizing and Accuracies for the Non-Cartographic ARC/INFO User"; Seventh Annual ESRI User Conference. 1987. 34pp.

Roblin, Hugh S. *Map Projections*. Norwich, England: Fletcher & Son, Ltd. 1969. 60pp.

Soler, T. and L.D. Hothem (1989). Important Parameters Used in Geodetic Transformations, *Journal of Surveying Engineering*, Vol. 115, No. 4, November, 1989.

Snyder, John P. *Map Projections used by the U. S. Geological Survey*. Bulletin 1532. Second Edition. Washington D.C.: U.S. Government Printing Office. 1983. 313pp.

Snyder, John P. *Map Projections - A Working Manual*. U.S. Geological Survey Professional Paper 1395. Washington, D.C.: U.S. Government Printing Office. 1987. 383pp.

Snyder, John P. and Philip M. Voxland. *An Album of Map Projections*. U.S. Geological Survey Professional Paper 1453. Washington, D.C.: U.S. Government Printing Office. 1989. 249pp.

Stem, James E. *State Plane Coordinate System of 1983*. NOAA Manual NOS NGS 5. 1990.

Wade Elizabeth B. and David R. Doyle. "Datum Transformation from NAD27 to NAD83." ACSM Technical Papers, Volume 3, pp. 27–36. 1987.

Index

Refer to last page for chart

NOTES

NOTES